Haird

Bob W

Nelson

Thomas Nelson and Sons Ltd
Nelson House Mayfield Road
Walton-on-Thames Surrey
KT12 5PL UK

Thomas Nelson Australia
102 Dodds Street
South Melbourne
Victoria 3205 Australia

Nelson Canada
1120 Birchmount Road
Scarborough
Ontario
MIK 5G4 Canada

First published by Thomas Nelson and Sons Ltd 1996

I(T)P Thomas Nelson is an International Thomson Publishing Company

I(T)P is used under licence

ISBN 0-17-490009-0

NPN 9 8 7 6 5 4 3 2 1

Printed in Spain

Acknowledgements:
Acquisitions: Alex Bridgland/Steve Berry
Administration: Jenny Goode
Editorial: Simon Bell
Marketing: Jane Lewis
Production: Hamish Adamson
Staff Design: Maria Pritchard
Design/Typesetting: Hardlines

Contents

Acknowledgements

The publishers would like to acknowledge the Hairdressing Training Board for the development of the NVQ and SVQ at levels 1, 2 and 3.

The authors and publishers would like to acknowledge the following photographic sources.

The author and publishers would like to acknowledge the assistance of West Kent College, Tonbridge, Kent in providing facilities for the following photographs.

Photographer: David Guy
Technical Director: Bob Woodhouse
Figures 2.2, 2.3, 2.4, 2.5, 2.6, 2.7, 2.8, 2.9, 2.10, 2.11, 2.12, 2.15, 3.2, 3.3, 3.4, 3.5 , 3.6 , 3.7, 3.8, 3.9, 3.10, 3.11, 3.12, 3.13e, 4.1a, 4.3a, 4.31, 4.32, 4.33, 5A.7, 5A.13, 5A.17, 5A.18, 5A.19, 5A.20, 5A.21, 5A.22, 5A.23, 5A.24, 5A.25, 5A.26, 5A.27, 5A.31, 5A.32, 5A.33, 5A.34, 5A.35, 5A.36, 5A.37, 5A.38, 5A.39, 5A.40, 5A.43, 5A.46, 6.39, 6.40, 6.41, 6.42, 6.43, 6.44, 6.45, 6.46, 6.47, 6.48, 9.1, 11.1, 11.2, 11.4, 11.6, 11.7, 11.8, 11.13, 11.38, 11.47, 11.52, 11.54, 11.58, 12.1, 12.2, 12.3, 12.4, 12.5, 12.6, 12.9, 12.10, 12.13, 12.14, 12.15, 12.22, 12.24, 12.31, 13.3, 13.4, 13.5, 13.6, 13.7, 13.8, 13.9, 13.10, 13.12, 13.13, 13.14, 13.15, 13.17, 13.18, 13.19, 13.20, 13.21, 13.22, 13.23, 13.24, 13.25, 13.26, 13.29, 13.30, 13.31, 13.32, 13.34 and 13.36

The following photographs originally appeared in *Milady's Standard Textbook of Cosmetology*, © 1994 Milady Publishing Company (A Division of Delmar Publishers Inc.) Photographers: Michael A. Gallitelli, Steven Landis, Eric Von Lockhart, Gillette Research Institute, New Image's Salon System
Figures on page 14 and page 15, and Figures 3.13a, 3.13b, 3.13c, 4.2, 4.3, 4.4, 4.5, 4.6, 4.7, 4.8, 4.9, 4.12, 5A.1, 5A.9, 5A.10a, 5A.10b, 5A.10c, 5A.10d, 5A.41, 5A.44, 5A.45, 5B.2, 5B.10, 5B.3, 5B.6, 5B.7, 5B.8, 5B.9, 5B.10, 5B.11, 6.1a, 6.1b, 6.2, 6.3, 6.4, 6.9, 6.11, 6.13, 6.14, 6.15, 6.16, 6.19, 6.26, 6.28, 6.29, 6.30, 6.33, 6.34, 6.35, 6.49, 7.1, 7.2, 8.1, 9.2, 11.28, 11.29, 11.30, 11.31, 11.32, 14.8, 14.11, 14.12, 14.13 and 14.28

Additional photographs as follows:
Price Associates: Figures 5B.12, 5B.13, 5B.14, 13.27 and 13.28
David Sparrow: Figure 4.1b
West Kent College: Figure 3.13c
The National Medical Slide Bank/The Wellcome Trust: Figures 14.16, 14.17, 14.18, 14.19, 14.20, 14.27 and 14.29

If any acknowledgement has been inadvertently omitted, the omission will be rectified at the earliest possible opportunity.

Introduction

ABOUT THIS BOOK

To the student

This book will provide you with the essential knowledge required to help you acquire the skills necessary for professional ladies' and men's hair-dressing. Within this is the underpinning knowledge needed to help you achieve the current National Vocational Qualification or Scottish Vocational Qualification (NVQ or SVQ) at Levels 1 and 2. In each chapter you will be provided with information and instructions on how to acquire practical skills. Colour illustrations will help you to understand the practical tasks. Each chapter also includes questions that you may use to test yourself (with model answers in chapter 15) and check your learning, together with suggestions for tasks to further your learning and help you to demonstrate competence.

You may use the whole of this book, or you may follow those sections which apply to your current needs, at the appropriate level. On pages 261–264 is a 'skill check' that you may use to identify your existing skills and which you may use to direct you to those areas that require development. The skill check may be copied for your personal use to chart your progress, and will provide evidence of your personal professional development in your job role.

Additional support material available

There are videos available to complement the information in this book, which will help you in the development of your personal hair-dressing skills.

To the trainer/lecturer

This book is designed to support the emerging hairdresser and may be used as a support to a structured programme of delivery, both as a course textbook and as a reference text. It will facilitate the flexible candidate-centred ethos of Vocational Qualifications by enabling those whose preferred style of learning is self-supported study to work at their own pace, providing the necessary underpinning knowledge together with instruction in how to exercise hairdressing skills. This book will enable the student to achieve a basic grasp of these skills. For those candidates who follow a more formalised style of directed learning, this book provides reference points as well as both visual and text direction in how to carry out hairdressing tasks.

The Personal Skill Check (see page 261) may be used by the candidate to identify any previously acquired learning and to chart and review progress towards developing skills and understanding. This chart may be photocopied for multiple use by the owner of this book.

INTRODUCTION

The quality of service and care provided throughout the entire hairdressing experience is a major factor in satisfying a client. Compare your own reaction, when you visit a business where you receive an attentive, courteous service and are kept aware of what the process is that you will experience, to your feelings when you visit a similar category of business where you are treated without courtesy, and are not kept informed about what the process is or how long it should take.

All members of the hairdressing team should be responsible for customer care, no matter what level they are at within the business.

COMMUNICATION

You will not be able to satisfy your client's needs if you do not, in the first place, establish what those needs are. Without understanding them you will be unable to establish a personal action plan to achieve in the most efficient manner.

Your style of communication with the client should establish a professional and caring relationship with them. The exact style you use will differ according to the individual client, the hairdresser/stylist and the salon procedures. At all times you must be courteous, friendly and professional towards your client. The novice hairdresser must take care to maintain this approach to the client at all times, no matter what their own personal feelings. Do not air your stresses or personal grievances with or in front of the client. If you have any problems with your work in the salon discuss this with your trainer/tutor/manager at a mutually agreed time, where confidential guidance and rational discussion may take place.

Salon procedures may determine how your client is addressed; if you use clients' first names, you need to decide how to greet a client whose name you do not know (a new client). Ensure that you are fully aware of any of your salon's guidelines for client approach. Ask your trainer/tutor/manager for guidance if you are unsure. You should ensure that your clients can understand your style of speech (pace, vocabulary or accent). If you have a communication disadvantage make arrangements to ensure effective communication with your clients. Discuss this with your trainer/tutor/manager.

Never assume that the client understands your communication. Check for signs of a lack of comprehension; these will include a vague or quizzical expression on the client's face, and a lack of response. If you feel that the client has not understood what you are trying to say be prepared to spend a little time to discuss it with them. Remember some clients may have communication difficulties: these may include hearing, language and sight limitations and lack of attention.

You must inform your client about any delay or disruption in the hairdressing process. The reason for the delay or disruption and the implications for your client's treatment should be explained to them, in understandable terms. Give your client a realistic view of how long a delay is likely to be; discuss options with your client, such as alternative appointments, alternative hairstylists or alternatives to sitting waiting. Should the delay or disruption be known about in advance your client may be contacted and alternatives suggested, therefore preventing confrontation within the salon. Remember that your client may have a tight time schedule and disruption, if notified far enough in advance, can often be accommodated, provided that it is not a regular occurrence.

> ❛ TIP: Unless you are aware of your client's wishes you will not be able to work towards satisfying them. Communication is the key. ❜

CLIENT CONSULTATION

Consultation with your client will enable you to identify any factors which may limit or affect the services and products that you use. This is the opportunity to determine the most suitable techniques, products and equipment to enable you to create the agreed effect, and that both hair and scalp are suitable for these intended treatments.

Effective communication between you and your client is essential before beginning the hairdressing process, to ensure that your client's wishes are met. The use of style books, photographs, fashion magazines, computerised style viewers and wigs can help as aids to understanding proposed outcomes. Your consultation will normally take place when both you and your client are seated, facing each other, discussing their wishes with regard to their chosen hairstyle. You as the hairstylist will consider the suitability of the requested treatment and hairstyle for the client. Here is a list of critical influencing factors and questions to ask yourself:

I the client's life style

I does the hair style fit the client's employment requirements?

I does the client's face and head shape suit the requested hairstyle?

I does the client's haircut suit the requested hairstyle?

I does the texture and length of the hair suit the requested hairstyle?

I are there any hair growth patterns that may affect the required hairstyle?

There may be occasions when the style/treatment requested by your client is not, in your opinion, achievable on or suitable for the client. Your negotiation skills will be required to counsel and guide your client towards a more suitable choice. You will need to be honest and sincere, and objective enough to justify your statements to your clients.

Records of previous consultations and services given to your client should be viewed, enabling you to check on previous products used and outcomes. Many salons maintain a written record of clients and their consultations/treatments. This will usually take the form of alphabetically indexed cards containing information about previous findings and the products used on the client, the dates of use and the outcomes of these services. There are computerised customer information systems available, offering the same facility as the written record, but often making retrieval of the information much easier. Maintaining these client records will provide a record should a customer complain at a later stage. It will also help to ensure continuity when a previous treatment is to be repeated. The information contained in client records should be considered confidential. Many salons have a policy that your client may not have access to this information. Check with your trainer/tutor/manager for advice on this before giving out information.

Always consider additional services that will enhance the finished look and make maintenance of that look easier and more realistic for your client. Your client will look to you, as their hairstylist, for advice and guidance about their look and about which additional services, such as colour or permanent wave, may enhance this look. Hair colour may be used to improve the overall look of the hair, or to accentuate features of a particular hairstyle. The use of permanent waves or straighteners may help in the style retention and enable certain fashion effects to be achieved. Your client may not fully appreciate the effect that these additions to the service may have, so suggestions from hairstylists are an important part of their responsibility towards their clients. While these additional services may cost the client more, they will be justified provided they add to client satisfaction in their look.

TIP: Failure to consult with your client effectively may result in loss of business to your salon, damage to your client's hair and scalp, and failure to fulfil your client's wishes.

TIP: Remember, your client must feel that they can trust your judgement and guidance. Honest recommendations and advice on additional services will produce repeat business from clients who want you to guide them in their purchase. Your clients will buy their hair care products from the salon with your guidance rather than from retail outlets who are unable to offer professional advice.

Hair structures, page 234

Figure 1.1 Ideal face proportions

 Special considerations, page 22

HEAD AND FACE SHAPES

The best results are obtained when each of your clients facial features are properly analysed for strengths and shortcomings. Your job is to accentuate a client's best features and play down features that do not add to the person's attractiveness.

You must develop the ability to recommend hairstyles for your clients. Each client deserves a hairstyle that is properly proportioned to their body type, is correctly balanced to their head and facial features, and frames their face to its best advantage. The essentials of artistic and suitable hairstyles are based on the following general characteristics:

I Shape of the head: front view (face shape), profile, and back view.

I Characteristics of features: perfect as well as imperfect features, defects, or blemishes.

I Body structure, posture, and poise.

Facial types

Each client's facial shape is determined by the position and the prominence of the facial bones. There are seven facial shapes: oval, round, square, oblong, pear-shaped, heart-shaped, and diamond-shaped. To recognise each facial shape and to be able to give correct advice, you should be acquainted with the outstanding characteristics of each.

The face is divided into three areas: forehead to eyebrows, eyebrows to end of nose, and end of nose to bottom of chin. When creating a style for a client, you will be trying to create the illusion that each client has the ideal face shape (see Figure 1.1).

Oval facial type

The oval-shaped face is generally recognised as the ideal shape. The contour and proportions of the face form the basis for modifying all other facial shapes.

Facial contour: The oval face is about 1.5 times longer than its width across the brow. The forehead is slightly wider than the chin.

A person with an oval-shaped face can wear any hairstyle unless there are other considerations, such as spectacles, length and shape of nose, or profile (see Figure 1.2).

Round facial type

Facial contour: Round hairline and round chin line; wide face.

Aim: To create the illusion of length to the face.

Create a hairstyle with height by arranging the hair on top of the head. You can place some over the ears and cheeks, but it is also appropriate to keep the hair up on one side, leaving the ears exposed. Style the fringe to one side (see Figure 1.3).

Square facial type

Facial contour: Straight hairline and square jawline; wide face.

Aim: To create the illusion of length; offset the square features. The problems of the square facial type are similar to the round facial type. The style should lift off the forehead and come forward at the temples and jaw, creating the illusion of narrowness and softness in the face. Asymmetrical hairstyles work well (see Figure 1.4).

Pear-shaped facial type

Facial contour: Narrow forehead, wide jaw and chin line.

Aim: To create the illusion of width in the forehead.

Build a hairstyle that is fairly full and high. Cover the forehead partially

Figure 1.2 Oval face

Figure 1.3 Round face

Figure 1.4 Square face

with a fringe of soft hair. The hair should be worn with a soft curl or wave effect dressed over the ears. This arrangement adds apparent width to the forehead (see Figure 1.5).

Diamond facial type

Facial contour: Narrow forehead, extreme width through the cheekbones, and narrow chin.

Aim: To reduce the width across the cheekbone line.

Increasing the fullness across the jawline and forehead while keeping the hair close to the head at the cheekbone line helps create an oval appearance. Avoid hairstyles that lift away from the cheeks or move back from the hairline (see Figure 1.6).

Heart-shaped facial type

Facial contour: Wide forehead and narrow chin line.

Aim: To decrease the width of the forehead and increase the width in the lower part of the face.

To reduce the width of the forehead, a centre parting with the fringe flipped up or a style slanted to one side is recommended. Add width and softness at the jawline (see Figure 1.7).

Figure 1.5 Pear-shaped face

Figure 1.6 Diamond face

Figure 1.7 Heart-shaped face

Profiles

Always look at your client's profile. When creating a hairstyle, the profile can be a good indicator as to the correct shape of hairstyle to choose.

Straight profile

This is considered the ideal. It is neither concave nor convex, with no unusual facial features. Usually, all hairstyles are becoming to the straight or normal profile (see Figure 1.8).

Figure 1.8 Straight profile

Concave (prominent chin)

The hair at the nape should be styled softly with a movement upward. Do not build hair onto the forehead (see Figure 1.9).

Convex (receding forehead, prominent nose, and receding chin)

Place curls or a fringe over the forehead. Keep the styles close to the head at the nape (see Figure 1.10).

Low forehead, protruding chin

Create an illusion of fullness to the forehead by building a fluffy fringe with height. An upswept temple movement will add length to the face. Soft curls in the nape area soften the chin. Do not end the style line at the nape – this draws attention to the chin line. Rather, create a line that is either higher or lower than the chin line (see Figure 1.11).

Figure 1.9 Concave profile

Figure 1.10 Convex profile

Figure 1.11 Low forehead, protruding chin

Nose shapes

Nose shapes are closely related to profile. When studying your client's face, the nose must be considered both in profile and in full face.

Turned-up nose

This type of nose is usually small and accompanied by a straight profile. The small nose is considered to be a childlike quality; therefore it is best to design a hairstyle that is not associated with children. The hair should be swept off the face creating a line from the nose to the ear. This will add length to the short nose. The top hair should move off the forehead to give the illusion of length to the nose (see Figures 1.12 and 1.13).

Figure 1.12 Wrong

Figure 1.13 Right

Prominent nose (hooked, large, or pointed)

In order to draw attention away from the nose, bring the hair forward at the forehead with softness around the face (see Figures 1.14 and 1.15).

Figure 1.14 Wrong   Figure 1.15 Right

> **TIP:** Symmetrical hairstyles are evenly balanced styles. Asymmetrical hairstyles are unevenly balanced but still aesthetically pleasing.

Crooked nose

To minimise the conspicuous crooked nose, style the hair in an off-centre manner which will attract the eye away from the nose. Asymmetrical styles are best. Any well-balanced hairstyle will accentuate the fact that the face is not even (see Figures 1.16 and 1.17).

Figure 1.16 Wrong   Figure 1.17 Right   Figure 1.18 Wrong

Wide, flat nose

A wide, flat nose tends to broaden the face. In order to minimise this effect, the hair should be drawn away from the face. In addition, a centre parting tends to narrow the nose, as well as draw attention away from it (see Figures 1.18 and 1.19).

Eyes

The eyes are the focal point of a face. Be prepared to create hairstyles that bring out the best in a client's eyes.

Wide-set eyes

Usually found on a round or square face. You can minimise the effect by lifting and fluffing the top of the hair and fringe area. A side fringe helps to draw attention away from the space between the eyes (see Figures 1.20 and 1.21).

Figure 1.19 Right

Figure 1.20 Wrong

Figure 1.21 Right

Figure 1.22 Wrong

Figure 1.23 Right

Close-set eyes

Usually found on long, narrow faces, try to open the face with the illusion of more space between the eyes. Style the hair fairly high with a side movement. The hair ends should turn outward and up (see Figures 1.22 and 1.23).

Head shapes

The shape of your client's head is just as individual as other physical features. As with the face, the oval is considered the ideal shape. Your goal when designing hairstyles should be to give them the illusion of an oval. As you evaluate your client's head shape, mentally impose an oval picture over it. Where there is flatness, plan to build volume (see Figures 1.24 to 1.29).

Special considerations

Very few, if any, of your clients will have a perfect set of features. Your goal is to analyse their features and accentuate the best ones. In addition you will need to consider the particular features of various ethnic groups.

Plump with short neck

Aim: To create the illusion of length.

Corrective hairstyle: Sweep the hair up to give length to the neck. Build height on top. Avoid hairstyles that give fullness to the back of the neck and hairstyles with horizontal lines (see Figure 1.30).

Long, thin neck

Aim: To minimise the appearance of the long neck.

Corrective hairstyle: Cover the neck with soft waves. Avoid short or sculptured necklines. Keep the hair long and full at the nape (see Figure 1.31).

Figure 1.24 The perfect oval

Figure 1.25 Narrow head, flat back

Figure 1.26 Flat crown

Figure 1.27 Pointed head, hollow nape

Figure 1.28 Flat top

Figure 1.29 Small head

Figure 1.30 Plump with short neck

Figure 1.31 Long, thin neck

Figure 1.32 Afro-Caribbean client

Afro-Caribbean features

Follow styling rules that relate to the particular face shape. If the hair has been straightened, set it on large rollers. If not, press it thermally with a large barrel iron. Either method will allow you to gain more control in order to style the hair according to design principles (see Figure 1.32).

Oriental features

Follow styling rules that relate to the particular face shape. Keep in mind that oriental hair is usually strong and may require more precise handling (see Figure 1.33).

EDUCATING YOUR CLIENT

Your client will require educating in how to maintain their hair and the style that you have created. This will include correct choice and use of products on their hair. Clients will need guidance in how frequently they should visit you in the salon to maintain their hair. Follow up services for clients with new looks may be offered as a salon policy. All clients should be encouraged to make return appointment reservations before leaving the salon. This will enable you, the hairstylist, to plan your work as well as helping to ensure an ongoing client relationship.

RETAIL AND HOMECARE PRODUCT SALES

As more products are added to salon operations, selling is becoming an increasingly important responsibility of the hairdresser. The hairdresser who is equally proficient as a hairstylist and a salesperson is most likely to be the one to succeed in business. Advising clients about the proper

Figure 1.33 Oriental client

❝ **TIP: Remember, your client will become a mobile advertisement for your work. It is important that your client is able to maintain their look to the best advantage. You will improve your efficiency if you educate your client in the care of their hair between visits.** ❞

products to use in their hair care programme will not only add to your income, but will better enable your clients to maintain the look you worked so hard to achieve. The sale of suitable homecare products should be considered an integral part of the hairdressing process and all part of the need to satisfy the client's expectations, the one service supporting the good work of the other.

The largest percentage of home hair care products are sold in the high street retail shops, where advice in appropriate selection and correct use is given usually by non-hairdressers. You are at an advantage for these reasons:

I You are a well informed professional.

I Your client will be able to purchase products which complement the products which you have used on their hair.

I Your client will have indicated their willingness to purchase, by coming to you for advice and a professional service.

I The ambience of hair care and beauty will set the mood for considering the purchase of products related to this.

To be successful in sales you need ambition, determination, and a good personality. The first step in selling is to sell yourself. Clients must like and trust you before they will purchase hair care services, products, or other merchandise. Every client who enters the salon is a prospective purchaser of additional services and merchandise. The manner in which you treat that person lays the foundation for suggestive selling. Recognising the needs and preferences of clients makes the intelligent use of suggestive selling possible.

Selling principles

To become a proficient salesperson you must understand and be able to apply the following selling principles:

I Be familiar with the features and benefits of each service and product.

I Adapt your approach and technique to meet the needs of each client.

I Be self-confident.

I Generate interest and desire, which may lead to a sale.

I Look for indications of interest in products and services. Clients may be nervous about declaring interest, but they may look at the product or linger by the merchandising stand, asking questions about the product or service.

I Never misrepresent your service or product.

I Use tact when selling to a client.

I Don't underestimate the client or the client's intelligence.

I To sell a product or service, deliver a sales talk in a relaxed, friendly manner and, if possible, demonstrate its use.

I If selling a product, allow your client to handle the item.

I Recognise the right psychological moment to close (complete) any sale. Once the client has offered to buy, stop selling – don't oversell, except to praise the client for the purchase and assure them that they will be happy with it.

I Do not be embarrassed when informing the client of the cost of the purchase; the product does have a value.

Types of clients

The hairdresser who is most likely to be successful in selling additional services or merchandise to clients is one who can recognise the many different types of people and knows how to deal with each type.

The following are four of the most usual types you are likely to meet. Each type might be treated in the way suggested.

I *Shy, timid type.* Make the client feel at ease. Lead the conversation. Don't force the conversation. Be cheerful.

I *Talkative type.* Be a good listener. Tactfully switch the conversation to hair care product need.

I *Nervous, irritable type.* Does not want much conversation. Wants simple, practical hairstyle and a fast worker. Get started and finished as quickly as possible.

I *Inquisitive, over-cautious type.* Explain everything in detail. Show him or her facts – information leaflets, brand names. Ask for the client's opinion.

The psychology of selling

Each person who enters a salon is an individual with specific needs. No matter how good a hairdressing service or product may be, you will find it difficult to make a sale if the client has no need for it. Thus, your first task is to determine whether the client needs or is interested in a service or product.

FURTHER STUDY

I Find out what services are available within your salon, how long they take and what they cost.

I Ensure that you are fully aware of the products that are available for retail sale in your salon and their particular features and benefits.

I Attending manufacturers' product use demonstrations will help you to learn about their use and their features and benefits.

I Develop your skills of negotiation with clients, particularly how to guide a client towards the correct choice of hairstyles.

Review questions

1. List the information required for the customer records retained in your salon.

2. To whom, within your salon, do you refer if the client expresses concern with service in the salon?

3. Suggest two indicators that a client does not understand your communication.

4. Describe how a new client is addressed when visiting your salon.

5. Which hair or scalp conditions may preclude hairdressing processes? What advice would you give the client with one of these conditions?

6. Which term is used to describe the coarseness or fineness of the hair?

7. Which term is used to describe the ability of hair to absorb moisture?

8. Does hair stretch more easily when wet or when dry?

9. Describe two strong hair growth patterns.

Figure 2.2 Brushing the hair

Figure 2.3 Hair sectioned and brushing started

TIP: Check with your supervisor on the salon procedure for looking after clients' valuables.

I Do not brush before giving a chemical treatment.

I Do not brush if the scalp is irritated.

Brushing stimulates the blood circulation to the scalp and helps remove dust, dirt, tangles and hairspray build-up from the hair (see Figure 2.2). Therefore, you should brush the hair whether the scalp and hair are in a dry or an oily condition. Do not use the comb to loosen scales from the scalp.

To brush the hair, first part it through the centre from front to nape. Then part a section about 1.25cm ($\frac{1}{2}$") off the centre parting starting at the nape. Holding this strand of hair in the left hand between the thumb and fingers, lay the brush (held in the right hand) with the bristles well down on the hair close to the scalp; rotate the brush by turning the wrist slightly, and sweep the bristles the full length of the hair. Repeat three times. Then part the hair again 1.25cm ($\frac{1}{2}$") above the first parting and continue until the entire head has been brushed (see Figure 2.3).

Avoid placing the hair under undue tension. If the hair is tangled, commence by removing tangles at the points, then work steadily back towards the root area.

Shampoo procedure
Preparation

1. Seat your client comfortably at your work station.

2. Select and arrange the required materials.

3. Wash/cleanse your hands.

4. Place the shampoo cape around your client's neck (be sure that the client's clothing lies smoothly under the gown and cape. See Figure 2.4.

5. Remove any hairpins and combs from the hair.

6. Ask your client to remove earrings and glasses and put them in a safe place.

7. Examine the condition of your client's hair and scalp to determine the correct shampoo choice, check for any contra-indications to shampooing: open cuts or sores on the scalp, contagious disorders.

8. Brush the hair thoroughly.

9. Seat your client comfortably at the shampoo basin, ensuring that your client is seated in such a position that their neck makes an efficient water seal between it and the basin (assuming that it is a back wash style basin. See Figure 2.5).

Figure 2.4 Completed shampoo gowning

Figure 2.5 Client at back wash basin

Figure 2.6 Testing water temperature

10. Ensure that towels are correctly located to protect the client. Two towels will be required. Some salons place a towel around the neck at the front of the client and then the second around the neck at the back. Other salons place one towel around the back of the neck, keeping the second in reserve for use when the shampoo is completed.

11. Adjust the volume and temperature of the water spray.

To avoid scalding yourself and the client turn on the cold water flow first and then gradually introduce the hot water until a temperature which is comfortable to the client is established. Test the temperature of the water by spraying it on the back of your hand or the inside of your wrist, as these areas are more sensitive to temperature than the palm of the hand. The temperature of the water must be constantly monitored by keeping one finger over the edge of the spray nozzle (rose) and in contact with the water (see Figure 2.6).

Procedure

1. Wet hair thoroughly with warm water spray. Lift the hair and work it with your free hand to saturate the scalp. Shift your hand to protect the client's face, ears and neck from the spray when working around the hairline (see Figure 2.7).

2. Apply small quantities of shampoo to the hair. First emulsify the shampoo on the palms of the hands. This will aid distribution and remove any chill. Beginning at the hairline and working back apply the shampoo with the effleurage massage technique. Work into a lather using the pads or cushions of the fingers (the rotary massage technique).

3. Manipulate the scalp using rotary massage.

a) Use pads of the fingers and thumbs working them in small rotary movements on the scalp.

b) Begin at the front hairline and work in a back-and-forth movement until the top of the head is reached (see Figure 2.8).

c) Continue in this manner to the back of the head, shifting your fingers back 2.5 cm (1″) at a time.

d) Lift the client's head, with your left hand controlling the movement of the head. With your right hand, start at the top of the right ear and, using the same movement, work to the back of the head.

e) Drop your fingers down 2.5 cm (1″) and repeat the process until the right side of the head is covered.

f) Beginning at the left ear, repeat the previous two steps.

g) Allow the client's head to relax and work around the hairline with your thumbs in a rotary movement.

h) Repeat these movements until the scalp has been thoroughly massaged.

i) Remove excess shampoo and lather by gently squeezing the hair.

4. Rinse the hair thoroughly.

a) Lift the hair at the crown and back with the fingers of your left hand to allow the spray to rinse the hair thoroughly.

b) Cup your hand along the napeline and pat the hair, forcing the spray of water against the base scalp area.

5. Repeat the process.

a) If necessary, repeat the procedure using the steps 2, 3 and 4 as outlined above. You will need less shampoo because partially clean hair lathers more easily.

REMINDER: In massaging the scalp, do not use firm pressure if:

I **You will be giving your client a chemical service after the shampoo.**

I **Your client's scalp is tender or sensitive.**

I **Your client requests less pressure.**

When you are shampooing excessively greasy hair, the shampooing may be more effective if the shampoo is added to the hair before water is added. This will aid the emulsification of the oil.

Figure 2.7 Shielding client's face during shampooing

Figure 2.8 Rotary massage technique

REMINDER: When you are shampooing very long hair take care not to tangle the hair by your massage technique. Drawing your fingers from the root area to the hair points will help to untangle the hair.

Figure 2.9 Rinsing shampoo from the nape area

Surface-active conditioners, page 35

Figure 2.10 Towel drying the hair

b) It may not be necessary to repeat this process when shampooing recently shampooed hair or when the hair is excessively fine.

6. Surface hair conditioning.

a) If required, a surface conditioner may be applied at this time.

b) Remove excess moisture from the hair by squeezing the hair in the hands.

c) Using your hands or a specialised applicator, apply the conditioner to the hair and distribute throughout the hair, using an effleurage massage movement, (see pages 36-37).

d) Rinse the excess conditioner from the hair, following the manufacturer's instructions.

e) If you are in doubt about whether a surface-active conditioner is required, consult with the hair stylist.

7. Partially towel dry.

a) Remove excess moisture from the hair at the shampoo basin.

b) Wipe excess moisture from around the client's face and ears with the towel, take care not to allow the corners of the towel to contact the client's eyes. Folding the ends of the towel back on themselves will help to prevent this (see Figure 2.10).

c) Lift the towel over the back of the client's head and wrap the head with the towel.

d) Place your hands on top of the towel and massage until the hair is partially dry (see Figure 2.10). Use the effleurage technique.

Completion

1. Comb the hair, using a wide-toothed comb, beginning with the ends at the nape of the client's neck. This will help to prevent unnecessary tension on the hair.

2. Change the towel around the client's neck, if necessary.

3. Style the hair as desired.

Clean-up

1. Dispose of used materials, and place unused supplies in their proper places.

2. Wipe the basin area clear of hair and water.

3. Place used towels in the towel bin.

4. Remove hair from combs and brushes and wash them with hot, soapy water; rinse and place in wet disinfectant for the required time.

5. Wash your hands.

What the expert says

Shampooing is one of the first skills that you learn as a novice hairdresser. It should not be regarded as an unimportant task to be carried out by an unskilled person. One of the first procedures that your client will experience within the salon, shampooing prepares the hair for most hairdressing processes and success in these subsequent processes may often depend on effective preparation of the surface on which the hairstylist creates.

The shampooist is an important member of the hairdressing salon team. When carrying out a shampoo, remember that you have the opportunity to create a rapport with your client. The shampoo should relax your client, so carry it out in a style which is likely to do this. While speed of work is important for business efficiency, this speed should be achieved without making your client feel rushed. A prepared and methodical approach to the process will enable you to achieve the speed but at the same time to relax and reassure your client that they are in the hands of a knowledgeable professional. By being adequately prepared, you will have all the tools you need at hand. This will help to ensure that your client receives a process which flows and is not interrupted by frantic periods when you are searching for the correct product or leaving the client to fetch tools that should have already been at hand.

There are opportunities for you to show your professional skill during the shampoo. Remember that you are the professional, who in most cases has a greater knowledge of the procedures and products being used. Advise your client in the correct choice of product, this may include the choice of shampoo or cleanser. Advise your client about appropriate conditioning for their hair. You will have a greater knowledge about the range of products used within your salon, your client has come to you for a service and your advice is part of that service.

Home-use hair care products may be suggested during the shampoo process, particularly suitable shampoos and conditioners. Watch out for signs of interest shown by your client in the products you are using. Retail lines which complement the products used within your salon should be available.

Salon cleanliness

Occasionally try to see the salon in the way that your client does. At the shampoo area consider what view of the salon they have. From the shampoo chair does your client see areas which require cleaning? Often from the seated position your client will see under shelves, basins and other fixtures which from a standing position appear perfect. However, when seated a client may get a different view.

THE CHEMISTRY OF SHAMPOO

To determine which shampoo will leave your client's hair in the best condition for the intended service you must understand the chemical ingredients of shampoos. Most shampoos have many common ingredients. It is often small differences in formulation that makes one shampoo better for a particular hair texture or condition.

The ingredient that most shampoos have in common, and it usually is number one on the list to show that there is more of it than any other ingredient, is water. Generally, it is not just plain water, but purified or deionised water. From there, ingredients are listed in descending order according to the percentage of each ingredient in the shampoo.

Classification of shampoos

The second ingredient that most shampoos have in common is the base surfactant or base detergent. These two terms, surfactant and detergent, mean the same thing, cleansing or 'surface-active' agent. The term surfactant describes organic compounds brought together by chemical synthesis (combining chemical elements to form a whole) to create wetting, dispersing, emulsifying, solubilising, foaming or washing agents (detergents).

The base surfactant or combination of surfactants determines into which class a shampoo will fall. The base surfactants used in shampoos fall into four broad classifications: anionic, cationic, non-ionic and ampholytic.

Most manufacturers use detergents from more than one classification. It is customary to use a secondary surfactant to complement or offset the negative qualities of the base surfactant. For example, an ampholytic that is non-irritating to the eyes can be added to a harsh anionic to create a product that is more comfortable to use.

TIP: It is useful to know the basic properties of the main classifications of surfactants.

Anionic	lowers the surface tension of water.
Cationic	attracted to the hair, has a positive charge.
Non-ionic	acts as a foam stabiliser.
Ampholytic	acts as a foam stabiliser, makes shampoo less irritating to the eyes.

TYPES OF SHAMPOO

The choice of shampoo is determined by:

l the condition of the scalp (dry, greasy or dandruff-affected)

l the texture and condition of the hair (damaged, porous, fine or chemically treated)

l subsequent hairdressing treatments (permanent wave and permanent hair colouring).

Shampoo manufacturers' guidelines should be followed in determining the appropriate choice for your client.

Those shampoos available today include those intended for use on:

Normal hair – these shampoos are designed to cleanse the average head of hair, leaving it in good condition for subsequent styling,

Dry hair – these shampoos will help nourish the hair, add moisture to the hair and make the hair easier to comb.

Greasy hair – these shampoos will be effective in the removal of sebum from the hair and scalp and may contain additives which will help to reduce the activity of the sebaceous glands.

Dandruff-affected – these shampoos will help to combat the causes of dandruff and to remove dandruff scales from the hair and scalp. Additives including selenium sulphide and zinc pyrethione are often included within these shampoos.

Fine hair – these shampoos are designed to reduce the softening effect of shampooing.

Artificially coloured hair – these shampoos are designed to reduce the colour fade caused by shampooing the hair.

Pre-perm – these shampoos are designed to cleanse the hair and to prepare the hair for subsequent permanent curling.

CONDITIONING HAIR AND SCALP

There are a number of hair and scalp conditions that may be treated by the professional hairdresser. It is essential that, in offering this service, the hairdresser is able to identify those conditions which may be safely treated and those which require referral to a medical practitioner.

Modern technology has enabled manufacturers to produce a wide range of professional treatments which may be offered by the hairdresser. In some cases these treatments take the form of 'one-off' products which may be applied to either the hair and/or scalp, independently of any other product used with your client. There are also treatment systems available which offer a range of products which may be used in conjunction with each other. These usually take the form of a range of shampoos (cleansers), treatment lotions or creams, styling aids and a range of 'take home' products which complement those used in the salon. These treatment ranges usually have a regime of use, which leads the hairdresser through the process of analysis of the hair and scalp, selection of the appropriate products and their correct method of application.

Hair conditioning
Corrective conditioning

Hair cannot care for itself, and once damaged is unable to repair itself.

Hair which is out of condition is usually rather dry, brittle and rough to the touch. This may be caused by the use of chemical processes on the hair (permanent waving, bleaching and tinting), the use of poor quality tools (rough combs or brushes with sharp bristles), excessive heat on the hair (too frequent or incorrect use of heated styling tools), your client's ill health or even the weather (excessive sun).

HEALTH AND SAFETY: Ensure that you thoroughly rinse and dry your hands after carrying out a shampoo. Failure to do this may result in dry, chapped skin (dermatitis).
If shampoo is allowed into the eye, the eye should be rinsed with copious supplies of sterile water. Should your client indicate that the shampoo is causing scalp irritation, this may indicate a possible allergic reaction. Alternative shampoos should then be used. In severe cases you should recommend that your client seek medical advice.

The hair and scalp, pages 233–252

TIP: A full awareness of the procedures for using these products is an essential part of offering them as treatments. Always follow the manufacturer's directions.

The result of this may be a roughening of the outside layer of the hair, the cuticle, or, in its worst state, the breakdown of the hair's structure, causing the hair to break.

Surface-active conditioning

Following a shampoo, the client's hair is often conditioned to compensate for the drying effect of these processes. A surface-active conditioner would be used. The action of a surface conditioner is to coat the hair. This fills the gaps on the roughened surface of the cuticle, making it easier to comb and less liable to tangle. It also helps to soften the hair. The action of the surface conditioner will usually last until the next shampoo, the effect gradually disappearing as the hair is brushed, combed and subjected to treatment.

To apply a surface conditioner following the shampoo, remove excess moisture from your client's hair by pressing it between your hands. Place a small amount of the conditioner on your hands and then distribute this throughout the hair, paying particular attention to those areas worst affected by any dryness. Gently work the conditioner through the hair using your fingers and then rinse thoroughly from the hair. Note that some conditioners are not rinsed from the hair: check the manufacturer's guidelines. A coating of conditioner will be left on the hair until it is next shampooed.

TIP: Always follow the manufacturer's guidelines when using a product.

Penetrating conditioners

These conditioners penetrate the surface of the hair. Their actions are varied but in the main their effect is to build artificial bonds which form in the cortex layer of the hair, replacing those natural bonds which have been lost due to the causes listed earlier. Many of these conditioners also neutralise the effect of chemical treatments on the hair, returning the hair to its normal pH of between 4.5 and 5.5. This helps to prevent any further action by the chemical.

Penetrating conditioners are available in liquid, cream and oil forms. The liquid form is the most suitable where softening the hair is not desirable. The cream format often has the benefit of both the surface-active and the penetrating conditioner in one product. Oil-based products usually consist of vegetable oils. Sulphonated vegetable oils are more easily shampooed from the hair following the treatment as they act both as an oil, conditioning, and a detergent, cleansing. When using a plain vegetable oil, apply to hair before it has been made wet, add shampoo and emulsify this with the oil before adding any water.

TIP: Always follow the manufacturer's directions when using these products. The manufacturer's advice on Health and Safety should be followed.

Protective conditioning

Some conditioners may be used to protect the hair during chemical processes. Certain liquid conditioners, called **pre-treatment conditioners**, may be applied before a permanent wave to even the porosity of the hair. This will produce a more even absorption, by the hair, of the perming solution. Those parts of the hair which are more porous and therefore require more protection absorb more of the pre-perm conditioner, therefore being self selective. Follow the manufacturer's directions at all times when using these products.

Certain cream-based conditioners may be used as protective barriers when perming hair. Those areas of the hair coated with the conditioner will not easily absorb the perming lotion. This technique may be used when root perming or when protecting highly delicate hair during a perming process.

A sunscreen surface-active conditioner may be applied to the hair, either as a cream or as a liquid spray. This lies on the surface of the hair and acts as a screen against harmful rays from the sun, which dry and lighten the hair.

Scalp treatments

Mild scalp conditions may often be treated by specialist treatment systems. There is a variety of product ranges available, including treatments to combat dandruff (*Pityriasis simplex*), greasy scalp (*Seborrhea*) and even forms of hair loss (*Alopecia*). As the cause of a scalp condition must normally be established before a successful treatment can be determined, and as this often requires the specialist knowledge of a trichologist, these products may not always be able to offer the remedy required. Therefore when offering a treatment to a client it is advisable to indicate that success is not guaranteed. When using specialist scalp treatments, always follow the manufacturer's guidelines on the method and frequency of application.

Following these treatments always update the client records. Remember, if you are unsure which treatment is most appropriate for your client, or how the treatment should be applied, consult with your trainer.

TIP: Take care always to wear protective gloves if recommended by the product manufacturer.

SCALP MASSAGE

This will help to stimulate capillary blood flow, which feeds the hair root and follicle. It will also help to stimulate the production of sebum (the hair and skin's natural oil) from the sebaceous glands which open into the hair follicle. Scalp massage will also relax and soothe your client.

Scalp massage may be given by hand or mechanically, and is usually given when the hair and scalp have been treated with a conditioning cream. This lubricates the surface of the hair and scalp, enabling the massage to take place without the client suffering discomfort.

Do not carry out any form of scalp massage if there are open sores or cuts on the scalp, if there is any contagious scalp disorder or if your client complains of pain or discomfort during the massage.

Hand applied scalp massage

Petrissage is a massage movement using the pads of the fingers, in a gripping, kneading movement (see Figure 2.11), co-ordinated together. Often when you start the scalp massage, the scalp is tight and therefore this massage should be started gently on the scalp and as the scalp manipulation loosens the scalp, the massage may become more intense, though never rough. The massage movement should follow an organised pattern over the scalp with both hands using an even pressure. Take care not to exert too much pressure on the sensitive areas of the scalp, the temporal and mastoid areas.

Effleurage is a stroking movement using the fingers and palms of the hands (Figure 2.12) and has a soothing effect, helping to distribute the increased blood flow.

Figure 2.11 Petrissage massage movement

Mechanically applied scalp massage
Direct massage

You may provide scalp massage by using the vibro massager, which is a gun-like apparatus with a spiked applicator. Ensure that the applicator is attached firmly to the vibro massager. Gently press the applicator onto the scalp and move in an organised pattern over the scalp in small circular movements (see Figure 2.13). Lift the applicator away from the hair and scalp occasionally to prevent tangling. This must be done more frequently if you are massaging the scalp of a client with long hair.

When using the vibro massager on your client for the first time, allow the client to become accustomed to its sensation by applying it for a few moments to the back of their hand. The duration of the treatment may be extended gradually, at each application, to a maximum of ten minutes.

Other applicators are designed for use on specific areas of the body:

I sponge – on the face

I suction bell – for deep skin toning

I flat applicator – for surface muscles

I hard vulcanite applicator – for large flat muscles.

Remember to ensure that all applicators are washed, dried and sterilised after each use.

Indirect massage

In indirect massage your hands become the applicators which make contact with your client's scalp. A type of vibro massager is strapped to the back of each hand, causing your hand to vibrate. You may then use your hands to make both petrissage and effleurage massage movements on the client's scalp.

Figure 2.12 Effleurage massage movement

THE USE OF HEAT

During the application of a cream conditioner heat may be used to aid penetration of the hair by the product, as well as speeding up any chemical processes. Moist heat swells the hair shaft, making this action easier. Heat may be provided in several ways including:

I the scalp steamer

I the thermal cap

I radiated heat

I scalp heat.

The scalp steamer

The scalp steamer is an apparatus with a hood that may be adjusted to fit over the scalp area of your client. It has a reservoir which holds a supply of distilled or deionised water. This water feeds into a small boiler which produces steam. This steam is fed to a series of jets which distribute it within the hood (Figure 2.14).

Before use ensure that the machine is clean. Check the inside of the hood for traces of previously used products and ensure that the reservoir has a sufficient supply of water. Pre-heat the steamer, and once steaming adjust any temperature settings and locate the hood carefully over the scalp area, ensuring that the hood and vents are adjusted so as to avoid steam escaping onto your client's neck. Ensure client comfort at all times, and ensure that your client is able to inform someone should they experience any discomfort.

Figure 2.13 Using a vibro massager on the scalp

The thermal cap

A thermal cap is a close-fitting hood with an electrically heated element, similar to that in an electric blanket, built into the fabric. Once connected to an electrical supply the interior of the cap becomes warm. This heat is conducted to the hair and any products lying on the hair. As the surface is water proof the moisture is retained. Care must be taken to ensure client comfort at all times.

Radiated heat

There are a number of appliances which may be used to radiate heat onto the hair and scalp. Some use specialised light bulbs to generate this heat; others use heating elements (Figure 2.15). Care must be taken to locate elements correctly around the head, to ensure even heating and to prevent 'hot spots' on the head. As the product's moisture is not trapped within any

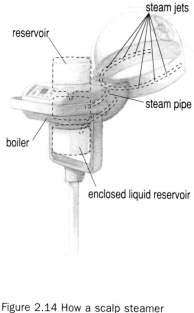

Figure 2.14 How a scalp steamer works

TIP: Never use electrical equipment if you do not know how to. Always read the manufacturer's directions or ask your trainer for guidance in correct use.

Figure 2.15 Accelerator in use on client

TIP: Some products, particularly oils, may become more liquid and run when heat is applied, so your client must be adequately protected by gowns and towels.

HEALTH AND SAFETY: Before using any electrical appliance make a visual check of all outer casings, cables and plugs. Should any loose connections or other damage be apparent, report this to your line manager. Do not use equipment which appears to be unsafe. Do not handle electrical appliances with wet hands. If you are not fully aware of how to use an item of equipment read the manufacturer's instructions or seek instruction from your trainer.

hood, check to ensure that the hair does not dry out during the process. If this happens moisten the hair.

Scalp heat

Scalp heat, if retained, may be used to aid penetration by conditioning products. The scalp area is enclosed within a polythene cap which, in turn, is enclosed within a towel. The polythene cap prevents moisture loss and the towels insulates reducing heat loss.

FURTHER STUDY

I Find out the features and benefits of the shampoos used in your salon, so that you can advise upon and select appropriate products for use on your client both in the salon and for home care.

I Many manufacturers produce treatment ranges which have cleansers (shampoos), which are complemented with hair and scalp conditioners and styling products. You should make yourself aware of these and how they are selected for the client.

I The hairdresser should be aware of what retail hair care products are available from non-hairdresser retail outlets so that comparisons may be discussed with your client.

I Develop your selling skills, look for signs, from your clients, of interest in retail products.

Review questions

1. List the range of shampoos used within your salon and indicate the hair and scalp types for which they are designed.

2. What effect can hard water have on the shower head at the basin?

3. On what occasions would you use 'dry' shampoos?

4. When shampooing, how is the water temperature tested?

5. Describe 'rotary' massage.

6. List two ingredients often found in 'anti-dandruff' shampoos.

7. What is the pH of normal hair?

8. Describe the action of a surface conditioner.

9. Give two occasions when protective conditioning may be appropriate.

10. Give two benefits to be gained by the client from scalp massage.

11. Describe Petrissage massage movement.

12. Give two contra-indications to the use of vibro scalp massage.

13. What benefits are obtained from using heat in conjunction with a reconditioning cream?

14. What fluid is used in the scalp steamer?

3 Drying hair into shape

This section gives you the essential knowledge to help you understand the processes of drying hair to create a finished look. This includes a variety of fashion styling techniques.

CONTENTS

I the hair type – curly hair may require more tension when drying to control or reduce the natural curl.

I strong hair growth patterns – for example, a 'double crown' may require more control in the drying process.

STYLING AIDS
Liquid styling aids

Liquid styling aids have the following properties:

I they help to make the hair more manageable during the drying process

I they prolong the life of the hair style (by excluding atmospheric moisture)

I they give the hair the necessary stiffness to enable the production of the required hairstyle

I they help to condition and moisturise the hair

I they compensate for the damaging effect that heat can have on the hair.
Liquid styling aids are usually applied to wet hair that has been towel dried.

Your choice of styling aid will be determined by the client's hair type, the required hairstyle, the features of the particular product, your personal preference and the salon's policy.

This information can be obtained by following the manufacturer's guidance notes. The trainee stylist may also follow guidance and ask advice from the stylist.

Blow-dry lotions are available in liquid form, as a single application phial and multi-application bottles, as well as aerosol and pump action. Liquids are applied by sprinkling onto the hair, spreading throughout using both your fingers and comb. Aerosols may be applied by directing the spray onto the hair, ensuring distribution by directing the spray throughout the head of hair and by combing. Take care: avoid applying too much of the product which will then run onto the client's neck, weigh down the hair and cause waste.

Mousse is a blow-dry lotion produced in foam form, making the product easier to apply and distribute by hand throughout all the hair or on specific areas of the hair. Apply by hand a sphere of mousse the size of a golf ball, distributing it throughout the hair using the fingers, followed by a wide-toothed comb (see Figure 3.3). Take care when first applying the mousse as it can be inclined to roll off the hair.

Gel is a styling aid which has a heavier consistency than mousse or blow-dry lotions. Applied from the palms of your hands, it is distributed throughout the hair. The gel may also be applied to specific parts of the hair using the pads of your fingers. Gel can be available in both a normal dry look when dry, and a wet look. The crisp finish left on the hair, if the gel is left to dry undisturbed, makes gel very suitable for sculptured/ slick looks.

These products are often available for a variety of hair types and degrees of hold, normal and firm.

Curl activators and moisturisers are usually available as a pump action spray. Spray this onto curly hair to gave a more controlled, defined curl. Direct the spray throughout the hair and distribute using a wide toothed comb and the fingers. These products are particularly useful on hair that is dry, difficult to control and fragile.

TIP: To enable you to select the most appropriate product for use on the client, you should understand the features of all of the styling aids used within your salon.

Figure 3.3 Applying mousse to the hair

TIP: If you are unfamiliar with any product you use on a client's hair, always read and follow the manufacturer's instructions.

HEALTH AND SAFETY: If you are uncertain about how to use a particular hairdryer, follow the manufacturer's advice or ask your line manager or trainer.

Figure 3.4 Fishtail and diffuser nozzles fitted to hairdryers

Styling tools

Your choice of blow-dryer may depend upon your personal preference, what is available and the type of style to be produced.

Hairdryers are available with a range of controls including differing air speeds and heat settings. For controlled drying a 'fishtail'-style nozzle can be fitted to concentrate the air flow to a narrow band. Diffusers may be fitted to many dryers to reduce the disruption to the hair caused by the air flow (see Figure 3.4).

Select styling tools that will not be adversely affected by the levels of heat used in the drying process. Remember that many plastic- and nylon-based tools will distort if exposed to heat for too long. The fine nylon bristles of brushes may soften or the teeth of plastic combs may bend. Vulcanite (hardened rubber) combs have a slightly higher heat resistance. Metal tools, such as aluminium combs, may be used when controlling short hair or producing waves of raised partings, *but they can become very hot, and if then touched on the client's scalp may burn the skin*. Bone combs have a high resistance to heat.

There are a number of brushes designed specifically for use when blow drying, including 'vent' style brushes which are designed to aid air flow and thus speed up hair drying, and radial brushes of a variety of diameters which enable you to dry the hair into curved or rounded shapes (see Figures 3.5 and 3.6). Watch hairstylists, demonstrators and your instructors drying hair and the range of drying tools that they use. This may guide you in your choices.

BLOW DRYING

This technique is suitable for a wide range of hairstyles on a variety of hair types and hair lengths. The hair dryer is used together with a variety of tools, including hands, combs and brushes, the choice of which depends on the style required.

Your best results will be achieved on hair which is freshly shampooed. Shampooing prepares the hair by cleansing the hair and enabling it to be stretched into a new shape. The hair can then be dried into this new shape,

❶

🔘 **TIP: Remember, do not handle electrical appliances with wet hands.** 🔘

Figure 3.5 Blow drying brushes

Figure 3.6 Radial brushes

> **HEALTH AND SAFETY: Never use electrical appliances when the cable is damaged or frayed in any way. Report any damaged equipment to your line manager or person responsible for maintenance.**

Figure 3.7 Blow drying at the nape

delaying elastic recoil, which it will retain until the hair is moistened again. Following the shampoo, remove the excess moisture from the hair by towel drying. Remove any tangles from the hair using a wide-toothed comb, taking care not to cause discomfort to the client, or damage to the hair, by excessive tension on the hair. (Fine porous hair is very easily damaged and broken while wet.)

Apply appropriate styling aids to the hair, taking care not to allow the product to spill onto the client's face or neck, and comb the hair into the direction of the style. Take care to avoid overheating the hair, as excessive heat can damage the hair and excessive heat on the scalp will cause your client discomfort. Avoid holding the air flow against the hair in one place for too long, as this may cause excessive heating and subsequent damage to the hair.

Having removed excess moisture start your blow dry at the lower parts of the hairstyle, those areas which will be on the underneath of the style (see Figure 3.7). If there is an area of the head or a part of the style which is likely to be particularly resistant to styling, this is often best dried first. Ensure that each mesh of hair is dried before moving on to the next, as meshes which are left damp will affect others which lie adjacent.

For smooth results the air flow should be directed with the direction of the hair. When achieving lift and volume, hold up meshes of hair in turn and direct the dryer into the root area (see Figure 3.8).

Use the dressing mirror to check the shape and balance of the hair style being developed.

Using the radial brush

Using the radial brush will enable you to dry the hair into curls or waves. Your choice of brush will depend upon a number of factors:

I The strength of curl achieved will depend on the radius of the brush that you use: the larger the radius, the softer the curl; the smaller the radius the tighter the curl. Curl strength may also depend on the amount of hair wrapped around the hairbrush when drying.

I The length of hair may determine the size of brush, as the hair will need to be long enough to be wrapped around the brush.

I Differing types of bristle material have differing characteristics. Fine, closely-set bristle tends to grip the hair; widely-spaced bristle may control the hair more easily and remove tangles.

I Your choice will often be personal choice. If in doubt, check with your supervisor.

Use the radial brush as follows:

Using the fingers, section off a mesh of hair and place it on the brush. Rotate the brush to smooth the ends of the hair into the direction of movement. Wind the hair around the brush and direct the air flow from the hairdryer in the direction in which the hair is lying (see Figure 3.9). Directing the air flow against the direction of the hair will produce a messy result as the shorter hair within the mesh will be dried without control and may produce a fuzzy appearance in the style.

To avoid damage to the hair by excessive heat do not direct the airflow at one place all the time. Keep the airflow moving over the hair. Rotate the brush to ensure that the hair is dried into a smooth finish around it. When working with long or very thick hair, drying can be more effective if you dry the ends of the hair first, gradually winding the hair around the brush and drying it progressively, working towards the root area. Take care when drying very long hair that the brush does not become entangled in it.

When drying fine hair (which drops the curl easily) or hair which is resistant to curl, leaving the brush in place as the hair cools will enhance curl retention.

If you wish to achieve lift at the roots, lift the mesh away from the head. The higher the mesh is lifted (over directed) the greater the lift achieved with the particular brush. Larger diameter brushes will produce more root lift. Flatter results will be produced by using root drag or incorporating the use both the radial and flat brush on the hair.

Using the flat brush

Using the flat brush will enable you to produce smooth, straight hair styles. There are two main styles of flat brush:

I brushes with closely set, fine bristles, which can be very useful when styling very short hair which may not be long enough to lie easily on the brush

Figure 3.8 Blow-drying to achieve root lift

Figure 3.9 Blow-drying with a radial brush

TIP: For safety, do not direct the airflow directly at the scalp as this may burn the client's skin.

Figure 3.10 Blow-drying for smooth bob with vent brush

Figure 3.11 Finger drying curly hair into style

Figure 3.12 Scrunch drying in the hand

I brushes with widely spaced, thick bristles, which are ideal when styling smooth straight styles where the hair length is sufficient to lie on the brush.

Generally the differences between brushes of these categories lie in their size, the number of rows of bristles and the style of base. Your choice should be the one which is most comfortable for you to use. The styles of base available are rubber cushioned back, solid back or vented back. The rubber cushioned back allows the bristles to move slightly and therefore flex with the hair. Both this and the solid back give smoother results on straight hairstyles. The vented back aids drying of the hair.

Using your fingers, take small meshes of hair and lay them in the bristles of the brush. With the air flow of the hair dryer directed onto the mesh of hair and in the direction of the hair, draw the brush from the roots to the points of the hair (see Figure 3.10). You will produce a smooth, straight result in this manner. When straightening wavy hair, slight tension must be maintained on the hair. If a slight movement is required, for example to turn the ends of a bobbed hairstyle either out or under, then roll the brush in the appropriate direction and direct the air flow onto the corner of the brush.

You may use either a brush or comb to control wet hair while blow waving:

I use a brush on long hair

I use a comb on short hair.

Shape the hair and direct the airflow into the trough of the wave.

FINGER DRYING

This technique is best suited to hair which falls into style easily, has some natural volume and movement and where an *informal* look is required. Your hands become the tools that guide the hair into position during the drying process. In many cases the body heat from your hands aids the drying of the hair. Drying is often aided by the use of the hair dryer. Your fingers will draw the hair into place either in a 'claw-like' fashion, the fingers taking on the role of a wide-toothed comb or brush, or will mould the hair by wrapping it around the fingers to produce movement in the hair (see Figure 3.11). Lift and volume at the roots is achieved by rotary movements of the hair at the root, using either finger pads or the palm of your hand and lifting the hair away from the scalp. Your client's head is normally maintained in an upright position except when producing volume in medium-length and long hair, when the head may be inclined downwards and then brought upright when the root area is dry.

SCRUNCH DRYING

This technique is used when a full curly style is required, usually on medium or long hair lengths. Compress the wet hair, into its curled shape in the hand and direct the air flow onto the palm of the hand, opening the hand to allow the access of the warm air and then closing to scrunch (see Figure 3.12). Continue to scrunch the hair as the hair cools after the heat has been removed. This will improve retention of movement.

When dressing a finished hairstyle you may use this scrunching technique to encourage movement in the hair. Place a small amount of styling aid, mousse, gel or wax onto the palms of your hands and then, without added heat, scrunch the hair.

NATURAL DRYING

As we have seen, wet hair stretches more easily than dry hair. During most drying processes the hair is stretched into shape and position and dried into this form. Elastic recoil is delayed when the hair is dried and remains in this shape until the hair is made wet again, either when shampooed or as moisture is absorbed from the atmosphere, when it returns to its natural shape and direction.

When drying naturally, the hair remains in its unstretched state, having been gently put into shape and dried undisturbed either without heat or by applying radiant heat.

What the expert says

Fashions today

Hair fashions today require a wide variety of drying techniques. With so many hair fashion leaders introducing their 'looks' for the season, your clients have a great wealth of creativity to call upon. At one time clients depended upon their hairstylist to inform them of current and emerging fashion. Today's business is consumer lead, and the consumer is informed by the media of what is available and what is emerging. This media takes the form of consumer magazines, some of which are related to the broad issues of fashion and others which are specific to their hair. These usually have features and designs from professional hairdressers. The media of television has realised the potential interest in fashion and several hairdressers now present their 'looks' on a variety of television shows.

This information coming to the consumer means that they will come to you, the professional hairdresser, with a number of preconceived ideas about how they wish to look. In extreme cases, due to the volume of differing ideas being presented via the media, they may come to you confused and wanting your professional guidance.

To be able to fulfil their expectations you need to be aware of current and emerging fashion trends and to be able to produce a range of looks for your clients. How do you do this?

The answers

As a professional hairdresser you must take the initiative to maintain your awareness of the fashion scene. Professional trade magazines can be one useful source of information and ideas. Often these magazines give you step by step guides in producing these styles as well as ideas for hair colour and other aids to enhance these looks.

Attending briefing seminars, often promoted by manufacturing houses or artistic groups, will enable you to maintain this awareness. There are a number of 'platform' shows, where well-known stylists or styling groups demonstrate techniques as well as presenting completed looks. Just as for many designer fashion exhibitions, much of the work demonstrated is not designed as 'street fashion'. However, ideas and concepts can be obtained from these and adapted for use with your clients.

New products or tools which enable you to produce specific fashion effects are often demonstrated at trade exhibitions, which occur throughout the year at a variety of venues.

Finding out

Information about forthcoming events is often given in professional trade magazines. Membership of a trade organisation can often be another source of this information.

Commitment

As hairdressers we should never stop learning new techniques or developing new skills if we wish to maintain a vibrant and growing clientele. Our clients seek a service which makes the most of their attributes in a fashionable way. As a successful professional you must be aware of this.

CREATING THE FINISHED LOOK

Having dried the hair in a controlled manner it will require dressing to give the finished look (see Figure 3.13).

Figure 3.13 Finished fashion hairstyles

Depending upon the result that you require this dressing may consist of brushing the hair into place using a brush of either closely tufted or widely spaced bristle.

For heavy, smooth, one-length looks the hair is usually brushed with a widely spaced, thick-bristle brush, brushing in the direction of the hair fall. To add texture to the finish, the hair may be brushed at 90 degrees to the direction of fall, usually back from the front hairline, and then allowed to fall into place. To add volume to heavy, smooth one-length styles the brush may be placed into the hair, which already lies in the direction of fall, and slowly lifted up allowing the hair to fall gradually. The surface should be smoothed gently, taking care not to dig the teeth of a widely spaced, large-toothed comb or the bristles of a brush into the volume of the hair.

For textured shorter looks the hair may be textured by drawing the fingers through the hair, in a claw-like fashion, either in or across the direction of the hairstyle. The 'vent' brush may be used in a similar way.

For controlled curly/tousled looks the hair may be scrunched in the hands, your hands may be used to position hair, to separate strands of hair, to add height by rotating the roots or by back-combing the hair, pushing back towards the roots on small meshes of hair.

To produce many fashion effects combinations of techniques must often be used. Be prepared to learn and adapt your techniques to suit emerging fashions. If you are uncertain of the technique to use ask your stylist/instructor for advice and guidance.

Techniques of back combing or back brushing may be used when dressing these styles, to achieve more height or control over the hair.

Finishing products can be used to assist you in dressing the hair, to enable you to produce the desired look and to prolong the duration of the finished look.

Back combing, page 197
Back brushing, page 198

Some products are applied to the hair from the palms of the hands. They may also be applied, using the fingers, to particular areas of the style or to particular strands of hair. Others are applied as an aerosol directed at the hair.

To enable you to select the correct products for the hair texture and for the required result you must learn about the features of the products available in your salon.

The sprays available include hair fixing sprays which hold the hair in place. Some are available for particular hair types and conditions, and they are often available in differing degrees of hold. In selecting, you will consider the required finished look and whether the style should move or if it should stay fixed in place. Gel spray offers an alternative to hair spray on dry hair, often being firmer. It is designed for use as a sculpting lotion, an aid to dressing the hair into position.

Gel may be used not only when drying wet hair but also as a dressing aid, using small quantities scrunched through the hair to create volume as well as on specific strands of hair to enable them to be moulded into place. Wet look results may be achieved using these products.

Wax may be used to give separation and definition to the hair and curl. It may be used throughout the hairstyle, having applied a small amount worked through the hair from the palms of the hands. Wax may also be applied to individual strands of hair using the fingers. Fly-away hair may be calmed using a little wax. On fine, soft, hair wax can sometimes be too heavy a product for use.

Dressing creams/mousses give control to hair and enables the hair to be sculpted and moulded into shape. These products are available in a range of strengths and are suitable for differing hair textures and style effects.

Gloss, usually a fine oil is available in liquid and aerosol forms. These give shine to the hair. Over-generous use of these products can result in a greasy look to the hair.

When applying hair-fixing spray to the finished look, avoid wetting the hair by holding the spray too close or by holding the spray in one place for too long. When using aerosol on fine, soft hair, the pressure of the spray may move or flatten the hair. Protect the client, their skin and clothing from the products being used.

TIP: When you use finishing products on the hair, if you are unfamiliar with the product read the manufacturers instructions and always follow these instructions. Remember, many finishing products are inflammable and must be used with care.

FURTHER STUDY

I Find out what the emerging fashions are in hairstyling and how these styles are created.

I Read the consumer trade press to find out about current and emerging hair fashion.

I To increase your range of skills practise a variety of drying techniques.

I Find out what effect the Control of Substances Hazardous to Health Regulations have on the use of styling products within your salon.

Review questions

1. Which bonds, located within the hair's cortex, are broken down and then reformed during the blow-dry process?

2. How much styling mousse is normally required when styling hair?

3. How should hair fixing spray be applied to the finished hairstyle?

4. What effect will moisture have upon the finished hairstyle?

5. Which factors will affect your choice of styling technique to be used?

6. How may height be achieved in the hairstyle through blow-drying?

7. When blow-drying, how is a smooth effect achieved?

8. Which blow-dryer attachment should be used when scrunch-drying hair?

9. What styling product should be used to help achieve separation and definition in a finished hairstyle?

10. What may be the result of applying too much gloss spray to the hair?

4 Haircutting

This chapter provides the essential knowledge of the basic techniques you will use to cut hair.

CONTENTS

INTRODUCTION

This aspect of hairstyling has, arguably, the highest profile with your clientele. Clients appear to think haircutting more important than any other hairdressing skill. Such is the profile of haircutting that there are a number of emerging salon groups specialising in haircutting, often to the exclusion of any of the chemical hairdressing processes.

Haircutting skills are acquired through a thorough understanding of the shapes and effects that may be produced in hair using a range of techniques with a variety of cutting tools. These skills are developed through practice, initially on wefts of hair (hair attached to a band or thread), then on training heads (lifelike heads with implanted hair, usually human). These tools will enable you, as a trainee hairdresser, to develop the basic techniques and manual dexterity required to create shapes in hair in a controlled manner. Eventually these skills must be applied to a live model. This will provide you with experience of a number of critical influencing factors, including a variety of hair textures, hair growth patterns, head and face shapes and lifestyles.

Learning to cut a number of individual haircuts without an understanding of the principles and processes which lie behind them will produce a skill which may not adapt to suit changing hair fashions and haircutting trends.

TOOLS USED FOR HAIRCUTTING

The quality and selection of tools is important in order for you to accomplish a good haircut. However, good tools will not produce a good haircut unless they are used in the correct manner. To do your best work you should use tools of good quality. However, as improper use will quickly destroy the efficiency of any implement, no matter how perfectly it might have been made in the factory, when starting to learn to cut hair it may not be advisable to purchase tools of a too high a cost until you have developed the skills to use them correctly.

Haircutting scissors

Figure 4.1a Range of scissors

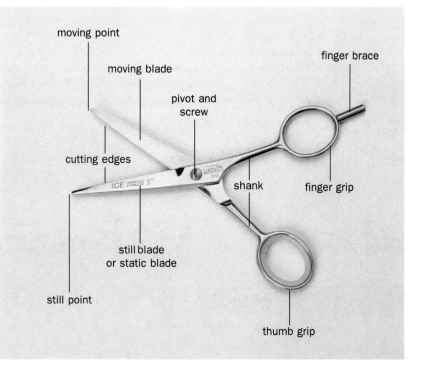

moving point

moving blade

finger brace

pivot and screw

cutting edges

shank

finger grip

still blade or static blade

still point

thumb grip

Figure 4.1b Haircutting scissors: the parts

Scissors come in a variety of sizes, shapes and finishes. The sizes of scissors are measured from the points to the opposite end at the finger grip (see Figure 4.1). The size is described in inches and may range from 3″ through to 10″ in $\frac{1}{2}$″ stages. Your choice will depend mainly upon two factors:

I What feels comfortable to use. The third finger and thumb should fit comfortably, and the thumb should be easily removed from the grip when palming the scissors. Plastic inserts can be obtained for certain scissors, allowing the size of the finger and thumb grips to be varied to suit the user.

I The technique of cutting to be used. Scissor-over-comb techniques normally require a longer pair of scissors than would be used to produce more textured looks.

The shape of the blade may be straight or curved, the curved shape being used when club cutting curved shapes in hair. The surface of the cutting edges may be smooth, or one or both of the edges may have micro-serrations. This helps to prevent hair sliding along the length of the blades as they are closed onto the hair (see Figure 4.3a).

The scissors may be made of metals of differing hardness. The harder metals retain the keenness of the edge for longer, but are more brittle. Scissors are available in stainless steel, chrome-plated steel and plastic-coated steel. Ceramic blades are also available.

Care of your scissors

I After use, always wipe you scissors dry and place them in their case.

I Use a light oil on the surfaces at the pivot.

I Always keep scissors sharp; the cut of the end of the hair is then much cleaner.

I Your scissors have blades which are finely ground; they require specialist sharpening.

Thinning scissors

There are many types of thinning scissors, the main distinction between types being the serrations on the blade. When the blade is closed, hair slides into the serrations and is not cut. The hair which does not slide into the gap is cut, and this action thins the hair. The more serrations, the less hair that will be removed. The wider the serrations and teeth of the scissors, the bolder the cut will be. Closely set, fine teeth will remove much finer strands; a pair of scissors with a single serrated blade will remove a greater bulk of hair than they would if both blades were serrated (see Figures 4.2 and 4.3).

⬥ HEALTH AND SAFETY: Don't keep haircutting scissors in your pocket, unless they are in a specialised wallet. ⬥

Figure 4.2 Thinning scissors with one serrated blade

Figure 4.3 Thinning scissors with two serrated blades

Figure 4.3a Smooth blade and blade with micro-serrations

Figure 4.7 Finger wrap hold

Figure 4.8 Three-finger hold

Figure 4.9 Holding razor and comb

TIP: When combing the hair, hold the razor and comb in the right hand (see Figure 4.9). When cutting the hair with a razor, hold the comb in the left hand. Do not put down the comb or razor.

TIP: When providing guidance to your client remember to be honest, tactful and sincere. Your client will respond to factual information provided in a clear, understandable and direct manner.

 Head and face shapes, page 18

Three-finger hold

Place three fingers over the shank, the thumb in the groove of the *shank*, and the little finger in the hollow part of the *tang* (see Figure 4.8).

When using the razor, keep the hair moist to avoid pulling the hair and to prevent dulling the razor.

CLIENT CONSULTATION AND PREPARATION

A good haircut is the foundation of every hairstyle and can change a client's view of themselves and their image.

Client consultation

In order to be aware of the required hairstyle, you must assess your client's needs and requirements and negotiate how these may be best implemented. Effective communication is essential, and there are a variety of tools to help you ensure that this takes place. These include style books, video imaging systems and wigs. Confirmation of the agreed hairstyle should be achieved before commencing the haircut, although this may be reviewed during the cutting process as it progresses. Consultation should normally take place before any work is commenced on your client. The following checklist of factors to bear in mind will help you to assess and advise your client:

- your client's requirements, personality, life-style
- your client's face and head shape
- your client's body proportions
- your client's hair type, texture, thickness and length
- any strong directions of hair growth (hair growth patterns)
- the suggested hairstyle
- your client's ability to cope with their hair.

Check the hair and scalp for any contraindications to the cutting process, these may include contagious scalp disorders, open cuts or sores on the scalp.

Gowning and protecting your client

The purpose of gowning your client prior to undertaking a haircut is to protect them and their clothing from hair clippings and any products used by you on their hair. Any method of gowning is acceptable provided that it protects your client and their clothing and is hygienic. Differing salons may have their own procedures for gowning the client. If in doubt consult with your line manager or trainer.

All items used should be clean, freshly laundered or disposable. Gowns and towels not laundered before re-use may pass infection from one client to the next. All gowning should be secured so that it does not come loose or fall during the cutting process.

A gown that is large enough to cover the client's clothing should be used, towels may be required when cutting wet hair, hairs embed themselves in towels, it may be considered more hygienic to towel dry the hair and use disposable plastic shoulder capes to protect the client. To prevent cut hairs from falling down between the client's neck and their clothing, insert a strip of clean cotton wool or a neck tissue around the neck area. These items are disposable and should be used only once.

Throughout the cut, loose hair clippings should be removed from the neck area using a clean neck brush. These brushes should be regularly washed, dried and sterilised. Do not allow quantities of hair clippings to build up around the client's neck during the cut, as this will easily become trapped in clothing. The application of talcum powder to the surface of the skin from a powder blower will help to remove clippings easily from the skin.

1. Having discussed the style with your client and assessed the hair for quality, quantity and length, gown the client and then shampoo or wet the hair, unless the hair is to be cut dry. The quality or condition of the hair will determine its elasticity and how well it will retain the dried shape. Hair that is dry or porous will lack shine and will not appear smooth and shiny once dried.

2. When wet the natural fall and movement of the hair may be determined. If this is assessed before wetting, the fall may be confused with the style introduced during the previous styling.

3. Check the hairline (front and back) for unusual hair growth patterns or characteristics which may affect the finished style.

➤ The hair and scalp, page 233

HAIRCUTTING TECHNIQUES

There are three basic techniques in cutting hair. These techniques may be achieved with a variety of haircutting tools used in a variety of ways. Their selection will depend on the required outcome, the preferred technique and salon policy.

❝TIP: While the risk of cutting your client is slight, the risk is always there. Ensure that you are aware of your salon procedure in dealing with this, the location of the first aid box within the salon, and any reporting procedures.❞

Club cutting hair

Club cutting involves cutting all of the hair so that all of its thickness is retained, reducing length but not volume (see Figure 4.10).

Figure 4.10 Club cutting

Figure 4.11 Maximising volume by club cutting

This technique is ideal when producing heavy, smooth hairstyles where curl or movement is not being encouraged. As all of the hair's natural volume is retained, it is ideal for use on thin, fine hair, where maximum volume is required (see Figure 4.11).

Thinning hair

Cutting the hair to reduce volume but not length (see Figure 4.12). This may be used to thin hair when it is too thick. It may be carried out over the whole head or just in localised areas (fringes and other hairline areas). Methods of thinning may be used to achieve lift, height or spiky effects in fashion styles. Thinning the point ends of the hair will encourage wavy hair to curl.

Taper cutting hair

Cutting the hair to reduce length as well as thickness. This may be carried out in a single operation (see Figure 4.15) or may be carried out as a two-step process, with a club cut followed by thinning. This technique of cutting hair can produce a natural taper to the hair, making it appear more natural for softer shapes. It will encourage wavy hair to curl, therefore being ideally suitable for hairstyles which require movement or curl. Straight hair which is going to be scrunch dried to curl will curl more easily if taper cut or thinned.

 Scrunch drying, page 46

 Back combing, page 197

Figure 4.12 Thinning hair with thinning scissors

Figure 4.13 Point thinning a fringe section

Figure 4.14 Thinning with haircutting scissors

Taper cutting will make winding thick hair onto perm rods easier and will also aid the process of back combing.

ACHIEVING TECHNIQUES USING HAIRCUTTING TOOLS

Club cutting can be carried out using either scissors (on wet or dry hair) or with clippers (on dry hair). The method of cutting using scissors or clippers over a comb is a method of club cutting the hair, achieving a graduated shape in very short hair (see Figure 3.13c, page 48).

Thinning can be carried out with thinning scissors, haircutting scissors or a razor/shaper. When using thinning scissors, note that if used on wet hair more hair will be removed than when used on dry hair. The term *texturising* is often applied to the technique of thinning the hair to achieve strong fashion effects, where the thinning gives the hair movement often associated with heavily defined changes in hair length.

Taper cutting can be carried out in one step using either a razor/shaper or scissors. Razor/shapers should be used on wet hair only and scissors on dry hair (wet hair does not separate so readily to facilitate the taper with scissors).

Figure 4.15 Taper cutting to aid back combing

PRODUCING SHAPES IN HAIR

Hairstyles are three-dimensional and when cutting hair it is not just the hair's length and outline shape that is changed, but the internal shape as well. There are four basic shapes that may be cut into hair. These may then be used in isolation from each other or may be used in combination, often to achieve fashion effects.

One-length or solid shapes

All of the hair within the style extends to the design line (the base line) of the hairstyle. This style produces the volume of the style around the design line, the weight line. If used on its own the hairstyle will tend to be flat on the top, smooth and weighty around the perimeter. If used on wavy or curly hair the result can be a very full effect.

Uniform layered shapes

All of the hair within the style is cut to the same length. The shape achieved in the style is the same as the head shape. As all the hair is cut to the same length there is no localised build up of volume in areas of the head, so the hair in the design line (the base line) will be wispy.

Layered: internal hair length greater than hair length at hairline (graduation)

The hair at the nape and side design line is the shortest in the hairstyle, gradually getting longer to the top of the hairstyle. Maximum volume is created at the point where the point ends of the top layer reach. This is the weight line within the style. This shape enables the hairdresser to adjust the apparent shape of the head.

TIP: Sharp cutting tools can be dangerous if used in confined areas, where there is a real risk that you will be knocked while working. Razors should not be left open on the work top, but closed and placed in a case or protective cover.

Figure 4.16 Achieving a full effect in wavy hair

Figure 4.17 Achieving uniform layered shapes

Figure 4.18 Layered hair: graduation where internal hair length greater than at hairline

Figure 4.19 Layered hair: graduation where internal hair length shorter than at hairline

Layered: internal hair length less than hair length at hairline (reverse graduation)

The hair on the top of the hairstyle is the shortest in the hairstyle, gradually getting longer towards the style's design line. This enables a long-hair effect to be produced but with volume and movement within the internal structure of the style. The volume is created not by creating a weight line within the style but by producing shorter hair which may lift, and hair ends within the style which may curl.

Figure 4.20 The one-length hairstyle

Figure 4.21 The uniform layered hairstyle

The one-length hairstyle (method of cutting)

This style requires that the weight be kept at the design line (base line) of the hairstyle, so the club cut technique should be used. The hair is best cut when wet as this gives maximum control over the hair. Very long hair will stretch while under tension, so take care not to place too much tension on it when cutting, as when released the hair will retract and the weight line will be lost. The process is :

1. Having sectioned the style, to control the hair the cutting of this style usually commences at the nape. Take small sections of hair, which may be easily controlled. Comb smooth and hold down flat to the head or shoulders and cut to the required length, allowing for elastic recoil. When cutting hair which will extend below the level of the nape hairline, it is advisable to keep your client's head upright or inclined forward slightly. The client's head should be central and not allowed to tilt to the side as this may lead to an unbalanced effect.

2. Bring down fine meshes of hair, in controllable sections, hold flat against the head and neck and cut to the position of the design line. The meshes of hair should be combed downwards to remove tangles and to control the hair. Keep the hair evenly wet while cutting so that you achieve an even level of hair stretch.

3. As you progress up the back of the head, taking fine sections of hair, holding in a downwards direction, the side sections of the head should be incorporated. This will help to ensure that there is no break or step between the back and sides. Hold the hair downwards, first cutting the design line. Allow for the additional hair length required to cover the ears and yet produce an even line at the design line.

4. Check the balance of the sides of the haircut by:

a) Drawing hair from identical areas of each side of the head. If the hair is of even length, the points should meet centrally.

b) Drawing the fingers down strands of the hair from both sides of the head, and check for level using the dressing position mirror.

5. Continue to progress up the head to the parting area. When directing the hair at the top of the head, comb it into the position into which it will fall when dry.

6. Check the cut when it is dry to ensure that all hair extends to the design line. This will allow for any uneven elastic recoil.

7. A fringe may be cut as an integral part of the style, or if it is not to be blended it may be separated off and cut.

8. Hard, solid design lines may be softened (thinned) by freehand cutting. This is cutting with scissors, pushing the scissors from within the hairstyle, in the direction of the hairstyle and closing the blades. To remove more hair the scissors may be angled slightly across the line of hair fall. Soft wispy effects on the sides may also be produced in this way.

9. Once completed, or if your client is to be consulted on the progress of the cut, show them the style using the back view mirror.

The uniform layered hairstyle

This hairstyle does not produce any weight lines in the hairstyle; it follows the shape of the wearer's own head. Additional shape and volume may be added to the style by perming and/or drying in a variety of ways. The hairstyle may be cut on either wet or dry hair and may be either club cut or taper cut, depending on how much volume is required in the style, and on whether the style is to have movement (curl or wave). The process is:

1. This shape may be cut in hair starting at any point of the head. This is normally either at the nape or at the top front of the hairstyle.

2. Take small meshes, which can be easily controlled. Having established the desired length, comb adjacent sections of hair out at 90 degrees to the scalp and, using the adjacent cut section as a guide, cut the hair to the same length. Failure to hold the hair out at 90 degrees can result in the hairs' length either becoming longer or shorter than that previously cut.

3. The hair may be tapered or thinned, using scissors or a razor/shaper in a specific area, as required for the hairstyle.

4. Ensure that your client's head is upright when checking for evenness and balance. Use the dressing point mirror to check the balance of both sides, placing the fingers through the hair and drawing the hair outwards.

The graduated hairstyle

The inner hair length is longer than the outline hair length but the inner hair does not reach to the design line. Graduation creates weight lines in the hairstyle. Figure 4.22 indicates the location of the design line, the weight line, the outline hair length and the inner hair.

The outline hair length or design line may be varied in length and shape depending upon the desired finished hairstyle. The location of the weight line can be varied by the angle of graduation, the weight line will be located at the top of the graduation, where the end of the longest hair reaches in the finished hairstyle.

A graduation may be cut by taking sections that are at 90 degrees to the design line (vertical sections) or by taking sections that are parallel to the design line. Your choice of technique will depend upon:

l the technique with which you are most familiar

l the technique used in your salon.

Cutting the graduated hairstyle usually commences at the design line, this being the shortest area of the hairstyle. The actual start point may vary: it may be the nape or the sides or around the ear, depending on the finished hairstyle which is required and personal preference. Take small sections which may be controlled easily, comb the hair to remove tangles and then hold it at the required angle. If taking horizontal sections, parallel to the design line, the section of hair should be held at between 1 degree and 90 degrees, depending upon the required angle of graduation and the position of the weight line. The smaller the angle, the lower the graduation and the lower down the head that the weight line will be located. By enlarging the angle, the weight line will be raised. Figures 4.23 to 4.26 will show this.

> **TIP:** While cutting hair, watch your client's body language for any indications of discomfort, as this may indicate concern about the progress of the haircut. If this is the case reassure them and address their concerns.

Figure 4.22 The graduated hairstyle

Figure 4.23

Figure 4.24   Figure 4.25

Figure 4.26

Barbering, page 203

Scissor-over-comb graduation

When a close graduation is required, the hair length being shorter than can be held between the fingers, a graduated result may be achieved by holding the hair in the teeth of the comb and cutting the hair. The comb is pushed upwards from the shortest length, into the longer hair. The cutting point is where the comb's teeth join the back of the comb. The comb's teeth should be angled to reflect the required angle of graduation. The comb should be moved in a steady continuous movement, the teeth angled outwards and the static blade of the scissors in line with the back of the comb. Electric clippers may also be used with this technique (see Figure 4.27).

The reverse graduation

The outer hair length is longer than the inner length. *Reverse graduation* does not create weight lines within the hairstyle, it does, however, allow height and movement within the framework of a longer hairstyle effect (see Figure 4.28).

Figure 4.27 Scissor-over-comb graduation

Figure 4.28 Reverse graduation

The outline hair length or design line may be varied in length and shape, depending upon the desired completed hairstyle. The degree of reverse graduation, how much shorter the inner hair length is compared to the outline hair length, may be varied to suit the hairstyle.

The technique of cutting usually starts at the shorter areas of the hairstyle, taking sections which are parallel to the design line. The hair is overdirected at more than 90 degrees to produce the reverse graduation. The greater the angle the greater the degree of reverse graduation (see Figures 4.29 and 4.30).

Figure 4.29 Producing reverse graduation (1)

Figure 4.30 Producing reverse graduation (2)

COMBINATION AND FASHION TECHNIQUES

Most hairstyles today require a combination of cutting shapes and cutting techniques to achieve their look. Examples of these are shown in the following illustrations. Figure 4.31 shows the use of graduation at the sides and back, linked with a uniform layer on the top.

Often a shape can be linked with a specific cutting technique for selected areas of the head. Figure 4.32 shows a technique for producing a one length cut linked with a fringe which has been texturised to produce a contrasting spiky effect.

You can give separation to those areas which lie onto the skin at the hairline by the use of freehand cutting (see Figure 4.33).

When using any cutting technique it is essential to view the progress of the style and respond to any effects which you did not at first expect, particularly when cutting a client's hair for the first time, when it may not always be possible to predict precisely how the hair will respond to the technique, method and length of the cut. Consult your client, explain what is happening and gain their confidence and agreement through your responsiveness.

Figure 4.31 Graduated haircut

FURTHER STUDY

▌ Find out about fashion cutting techniques and what effects they may produce in hair. Use trade magazines, videos and demonstrations to do this.

▌ All hair cutting techniques fall into one of the three categories: clubbing, thinning or tapering. Try to place the methods that you know into the appropriate technique category.

▌ Build a portfolio of current and emerging hairstyles and the techniques and methods used to achieve these. This will form a useful reference document for you in your work.

Figure 4.32 One length cut with spiky fringe

Review questions

1. Suggest two factors which may affect your choice of haircut for a client.
2. What is the purpose of gowning your client for a haircut?
3. For control, how should hair cutting scissors be held?
4. What is the name given to the hair cutting technique which reduces length but retains all of the hair's natural volume?
5. Which hair cutting technique will encourage wavy hair to curl?
6. Give another name for a layered look where the inner hair lengths are longer than the outer hair lengths.
7. What is a weight line?
8. How may the balance of the haircut be checked?
9. What advantage does scissor-over-comb graduation have over other methods of graduating?
10. Should a haircutting razor/shaper be used on **wet** or **dry** hair?

Figure 4.33 Effect of freehand cutting on hairline

lotions have also been developed to compensate for hair that is not equally porous all over.

Virtually all permanent waves are achieved with a two-step chemical process:

1. Waving lotion, which softens or breaks the internal structure of the hair.

2. Neutraliser, which re-hardens or re-bonds the internal structure of the hair.

The pH scale

This 14 point scale is used to indicate the acidity or alkalinity of a substance. The symbol pH (potential Hydrogen) refers to the quantity of hydrogen ions present. The centre of the scale (7) is neutral and is a point which is neither acid nor alkali. The further from the central point the higher the level of either acidity (pH of less than 7) or alkalinity (pH of over 7). The diagram (see Figure 5A.4) indicates the relative pH of a number of hair-dressing-related substances.

Figure 5A.4 Relative pH of hairdressing substances

HEALTH AND SAFETY: Care should be taken when handling any substance the pH of which falls near the extremes of the scale, as it may cause injury to the skin.

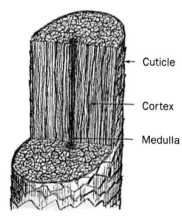

Figure 5A.4b Structure of a hair

- Cuticle
- Cortex
- Medulla

Alkaline perms

The main active ingredient (or 'reducing agent') in alkaline perms, ammonium thioglycolate, is a chemical compound made up of ammonium hydroxide and thioglycolic acid. The pH of alkaline waving lotions generally falls within the range 8.2 to 9.6, depending on the amounts of ammonium hydroxide present. Because the lotion is more alkaline, the cuticle layers swell slightly and open, allowing the solution to penetrate more quickly than acid-balanced lotions. Some alkaline perms are wound with perm lotion ('pre-damping'), others are wound with water, the perm lotion being applied after all the hair has been wound ('post-damping'). Some require a plastic cap (to retain scalp heat) for processing, others do not. Therefore, it is extremely important to read the manufacturer's instructions for use before beginning.

The benefits of alkaline perms are:

- strong curl patterns

- fast processing time (varies from 5 to 20 minutes)

- room temperature processing.

Generally, alkaline perms should be used when:

- perming resistant hair

- a strong/tight curl is desired

- the client has a history of early curl relaxation.

Acid-balanced perms

The main active ingredient in acid-balanced waving lotions is glycerol monothioglycolate, which effectively reduces the pH. This lower pH is gentler on the hair and typically gives a softer curl than alkaline cold waves. Acid-balanced perms have a pH range of approximately 4.5 to 7.9 and usually penetrate the hair more slowly. Thus, they require a longer processing time and heat to develop curl. Heat is produced in one of two ways:

1. The perm is activated by heat created chemically within the product. This method is called exothermic.

2. The perm is activated by an outside heat source, usually a conventional hood-type hair dryer. This method is called endothermic.

Recent advances in acid-balanced perm chemistry, however, have made it possible to process some acid-balanced perms at room temperature without heat. These newer acid-balanced perms usually have a slightly higher pH but still contain glycerol monothioglycolate as the active ingredient.

All acid-balanced perms are water wrapped, require a plastic cap (to retain scalp heat), and may or may not require a pre-heated hood dryer for processing. Read the manufacturer's perm directions carefully before starting the perm.

The benefits of acid-balanced perms are:

I softer curl patterns

I slower, but more controllable processing time (usually 15 to 25 minutes)

I gentler treatment for delicate hair types.

Generally, acid-balanced perms are used when:

I perming delicate/fragile or colour-treated hair

I soft, natural curl or wave pattern is desired

I style support, rather than strong curl, is required.

The chemistry of neutralisers

Neutralisers for both acid-balanced and alkaline perms have the same important function: to permanently establish the new curl shape. Neutralising is a very important step in the perming process. If the hair is not properly neutralised, the curl will relax or straighten after one or two shampooings. Generally, today's neutralisers are composed of a relatively small percentage of hydrogen peroxide, an oxidising agent, at an acidic pH. An alternative oxidising agent is sodium bromate. As with waving lotions, there are slightly different procedures recommended for individual products. To achieve the best possible results, read and follow the manufacturer's directions.

HAIR STRUCTURE AND PERMING

Whether using an acid-balanced or alkaline formula, all perms subject the hair to two different actions:

I physical action – wrapping sections of hair around a perm rod

I chemical action – created first by reducing agent (waving lotion) and second by an oxidising agent (neutraliser).

Since both of these actions work together to create a change in the internal structure of the hair, it is important to understand the composition of hair and how it is affected during perming.

TIP: If the presence of previous, unknown chemical treatments is apparent, carry out an incompatibility test to test for the presence of metallic salts on the hair. See page 138 for details of this test.

I How your client's hairstyle relates to overall personal image. Is your client concerned about current fashion trends?

I Your client's previous experience with perming. What did he or she like or dislike about past perm services?

Once you learn what questions to ask and how to ask them, the consultation with your perm client takes only a few minutes. It is time well spent, however, because the consultation helps establish your credibility as a professional. It inspires your client's confidence in your technical and creative abilities, and makes the perming experience more satisfactory for both of you.

Keep the vital information you learn during the client consultation as a permanent record, either written or computerised, along with other important data, including the client's address and both home and business telephone numbers. Here is an example of an organised format for maintaining client records:

PERMANENT WAVE RECORD

Name...Tel. ....

Address ....

....

DESCRIPTION OF HAIR

Length	Texture	Type		Porosity
☐ short	☐ coarse	☐ normal	☐ very porous	☐ slightly porous
☐ medium	☐ medium	☐ resistant		
☐ long	☐ fine	☐ tinted	☐ moderately porous	☐ resistant
		☐ highlighted		
		☐ bleached	☐ normal	

Condition

☐ very good	☐ good	☐ fair	☐ poor	☐ dry	☐ oily

Tinted with ....

Previously permed with ....

TYPE OF PERM

☐ alkaline	☐ acid	☐ body wave	☐ other

No. of rods.............................Lotion ....Strength..................

Results

☐ good	☐ poor	☐ too tight	☐ too loose

Date	Perm used	Stylist	Date	Perm used	Stylist
....	....		....	....	
....	....		....	....	
....	....		....	....	

Other side of Record, continue with:

Date	Perm used	Stylist	Date	Perm used	Stylist

Figure 5A.8 A client record sheet

What the expert says

A major contribution to the financial success of the salon is based upon the provision of chemical services. A satisfied client will make return visits to the salon. Perming can enable you to provide a full and satisfying service for your clients.

No matter what your role within the salon, you can help to provide the service. At reception the correct booking and phasing of appointments supports a smooth delivery of the service. As an assistant, the preparation of the working area and the provision of the correct tools, in the correct place at the appropriate time will support the service.

The stylist's skill will come about as a result of full product knowledge and extensive practice in all aspects of the perming process, including client consultation as well as the actual winding/wrapping of the perm.

Remember that in order to satisfy your client's expectations, you must provide the relevant support for them to care for their new perm between visits. This will include advice and guidance on drying techniques and the frequency of salon visits. Home haircare products should be suggested and their method of use described. If your client is willing to incur the expense of this chemical service they will want their hair to look good at all times.

PERM PREPARATION
Pre-perm analysis

After the client consultation, you must analyse the overall condition of your client's hair and scalp. This analysis is essential for you to determine:

I If it is safe and advisable to proceed with the perm service. The hair must be in good condition and have the necessary strength to accept a chemical alteration to achieve a successful perm.

I Which perm product should be chosen for the best results on the particular hair type.

I Which perm technique should be used: curler/rod and parting sizes and winding/wrapping pattern.

First, examine the scalp for abrasions, irritations, open sores or contagious disorders. If any of these exist, do not give the perm. Minor abrasions may be protected by using petroleum jelly BP as a barrier between the skin and the lotion. Next, judge the physical characteristics of the hair with regard to these important criteria: porosity, density, texture and length. Finally, determine the overall condition of the hair. Observe if the hair has been previously treated with chemicals: perm, tint, bleach, highlighting (frosting, dimensionally coloured). This will guide you in choosing the appropriate perm.

Check with your client for the previous use of products on the hair which may be incompatible with the perming process. Products which contain metallic salts, (compound Henna, hair colour restorers, progressive hair dyes and metallic coloured hair sprays) leave traces of salts on the hair which react with the process. If the presence of these salts is detected it is not safe to proceed with the perming process until all traces are removed. If you are in doubt if there are salts present, carry out an incompatibility test on a sample of the hair

Determining porosity

Porosity refers to the hair's capacity to absorb moisture. There is a direct relationship between the hair's porosity, the type of perm (acid-balanced or alkaline) you will use, and the strength of waving lotion you will choose.

The processing time for any perm depends more on hair porosity than any other factor. The more porous the hair, the less processing time it takes, and the milder the waving solution required. Hair porosity is affected by such factors as excessive exposure to sun and wind, use of harsh shampoos, tints and lighteners, previous perms and use of thermal styling appliances.

Porous hair might be dry – even very dry. If hair is tinted, bleached, has been exposed to the sun or was over-processed by a previous perm, it will absorb liquids readily. Soft, fine, thin hair usually has a thin cuticle so it will absorb liquids quickly and easily. Rough, dull-looking hair and hair that tangles easily is also likely to be porous.

While the hair is dry, check porosity in three different areas: front hairline, in front of the ear and in the crown area. Select a single strand of

CAUTION: If pre-perm analysis is not correct, poor curl development or hair damage can result.

 Incompatability test, see page 138

Figure 5A.9 Testing for hair porosity

hair, hold the end securely between the thumb and first finger of one hand and slide the thumb and first finger of the other hand from the hair end to the scalp.

If the hair feels smooth and the cuticle is dense and hard, it is considered resistant and will not absorb liquids or perm lotion easily. If you can feel a slight roughness, this tells you that the cuticle is open and that the hair is porous and will absorb liquids more readily (see Figure 5A.9).

Poor porosity (resistant hair)

Hair with the cuticle layer lying close to the hair shaft. This type of hair absorbs waving lotion slowly and usually requires a longer processing time and/or a strong waving lotion.

Good porosity (normal hair)

Hair with the cuticle layer slightly raised from the hair shaft. Hair of this type can absorb moisture or chemicals in an average amount of time.

Porous (tinted, lightened or previously chemically treated) hair

Hair that has been made porous by various treatments or styling. This type of hair absorbs lotion very quickly and requires the shortest processing time. Use either an acid-balanced perm or a very mild alkaline wave.

Over-porous hair (a result of over-processing)

This type of hair is very damaged, dry, fragile and brittle. Until the hair has been reconditioned or the damaged part has been removed by cutting, it should not be permed.

If hair is unevenly porous (usually porous or over porous at the ends with good to poor porosity near the scalp), a pre-wrap lotion, specifically designed to even out the porosity, is recommended to achieve even curl results and help prevent over-processing porous ends (see Figure 5A.10a–d).

Figure 5A.10a Normal (moderate porosity)

Figure 5A.10b Resistant (poor porosity)

Figure 5A.10c Tinted (extreme porosity)

Figure 5A.10d Damaged (over-porous hair)

Determining texture

Texture refers to how thick or thin (in diameter) each individual hair is. Fine hair has a small diameter; coarse hair has a large diameter. You can feel whether hair is fine, coarse, or medium when a single dry strand is held between the fingers.

The texture and porosity together are used to determine the processing time of the waving lotion. Although porosity is the more important of the two, texture does play an important role in estimating processing time. Fine hair with a small diameter becomes saturated with waving lotion more quickly than coarse hair with a large diameter, even if both are of equal porosity. However, when coarse hair is porous, it processes faster than fine hair that is not porous.

A perm adds body to hair that appears limp, lifeless, and does not hold a style very long. For coarse, wiry hair, a perm provides greater manageability in styling (see Figure 5A.11a–c).

Testing elasticity

Elasticity is the ability of hair to stretch and then return to its original length. To test for elasticity, stretch a single dry hair. If the hair breaks under very slight strain, it has little or no elasticity. Other signs of poor elasticity include a spongy feel when the hair is wet and/or hair that tangles easily. When hair is completely lacking in elasticity (for example, extremely damaged hair), it will not take a satisfactory permanent wave. The greater the degree of elasticity, the longer the wave will remain in the hair, because less relaxation of the hair occurs. Hair with good elastic qualities can be stretched by 20% of its length without breaking (see Figure 5A.12).

Assessing density

Density, or thickness, refers to the number of hairs per square centimetre on your client's head. Density is one characteristic that determines the size of the partings you will use. Thick hair (many hairs per square centimetre) will require small partings on each rod. Too much hair on the rod can result in a weak curl, especially at the scalp.

If hair is thin (few hairs per square centimetre), slightly larger partings can be used, but avoid stretching or pulling the hair towards the rod because this can cause hair breakage or straight, misdirected hair at the scalp.

Hair length and perming

Hair that is 5 cm to 15 cm long is considered ideal for perming. Hair should be long enough to make at least 2.5 turns around the rod. To perm hair longer than 15 cm, smaller partings must be used to allow the waving lotion and neutraliser to penetrate more easily and thoroughly.

Perm lotion selection

The type of perm lotion you choose depends on the total evaluation of your client's hair and wishes during the consultation and pre-perm analysis. The following is a general guide to help you decide whether to use an alkaline or an acid-balanced perm.

Figure 5A.11a Coarse; b Medium; c Fine

Figure 5A.12 Testing for elasticity

Hair type	Type of perm lotion
Coarse, resistant	Alkaline lotion wind or alkaline post-damp
Fine, resistant	Alkaline lotion wind or alkaline post-damp
Normal	Alkaline post-damp or acid-lotion
Normal, porous	Alkaline post-damp or acid-lotion
Normal, delicate	Acid-lotion
Tinted, non-porous	Alkaline post-damp or acid-lotion
Tinted, porous	Acid-lotion
Highlighted/frosted/dimensionally coloured	Acid-lotion
Highlighted, tinted	Acid-lotion
Bleached	Acid-lotion

Today's perm products offer a wide selection of special features and formulas for all hair types. There are alkaline formulas for bleached hair and acid-balanced formulas for resistant hair. Each formula gives excellent results if you choose the perm carefully and follow the manufacturer's directions.

Pre-perm shampooing

Today, there are shampoos specifically formulated for pre-perm cleansing that thoroughly yet gently cleanse the hair. Use of these shampoos is recommended for optimal results.

When analysing a client's hair before perming, you might notice that the hair looks and feels coated. This coating might be the build-up of shampoo or conditioners, improper rinsing, resins from styling products or hair spray, or mineral deposits from hard water. This coating can prevent penetration of the waving lotion and interfere with perm results. It is very important for the hair to be free of all coatings before beginning any perm.

Begin the process by wetting the hair, applying the shampoo, and gently working into a lather. If the hair is extremely coated let the shampoo remain in the hair for several minutes before rinsing. Rinse thoroughly to remove all shampoo and dissolved build-up. Towel blot excess water from the hair. For more information about the shampooing procedure read the section headed 'Shampooing' on pages 28-32. If you are in doubt about the selection of the appropriate shampoo to use consult your supervisor or the stylist.

Pre-perm cutting or shaping

If your client has chosen a hairstyle which is the same or very similar to the design he or she currently has, reshape the style using either scissors or a razor. If the finished style requires texturising or thinning of the ends, wait until after giving the perm to texturise. Over-tapered or thinned ends are more difficult to wrap smoothly and accurately. Irregular effects cut into hair can be difficult to wind without distortion of the hair. Lightly tapering thick hair before winding can aid the winding process.

If your client wants a completely new style, rough cut the hair into an approximation of the final shape. After the perm is completed, you can finish shaping the style more exactly.

Perm curlers and rods

Correct selection of perm curler or rod size is essential for successful perm results. The size of curler determines the size of curl created by the waving process. Perm curlers are typically made of plastic and come in varying sizes. They range in diameter (distance through the centre of the curler from side to side) from 0.3 to 1.9 cm. They are usually colour-coded to identify their size easily.

Perm curlers are also available in three lengths: short, medium and long (4.4 to 8.8 cm). Curlers of all diameters are available in long lengths. Medium and short lengths are not always available in all diameters. These shorter curlers are used for wrapping small or awkward sections.

As well as the traditional shape of perm curlers, there are a range of alternatives, some especially designed to achieve specific shapes in the hair. These include spiral curlers, rick-rack sticks, triangular curlers, flexible curlers and crimping shapers.

Types of curlers

There are two types of curlers: concave and straight. Concave curlers have a small diameter in the centre area and gradually increase to their largest diameter at the ends, resulting in a tighter curl at the hair ends, with a

NOTE: While shampooing or doing any pre-perm preparation of a client's hair, you should avoid vigorous brushing, combing, pulling or rubbing that can cause the scalp to become sensitive to perm solutions.

TIP: When selecting perm rods for use with acid perms, choosing a size smaller than the required curl size can help to reduce the effect of curl drop, sometimes experienced with this type of perm.

Figure 5A.13 Perm curlers, or rods, colour coded according to size

looser, wider curl at the scalp. The diameter of the straight curlers is the same throughout their length, creating an even-sized curl from end to scalp.

All curlers have some means of securing the hair on the curler to prevent the curl from unwinding. Usually an elastic band, with a fastening button or loop attached to the end, stretches across the wound hair and secures it when the button or loop is inserted into the opposite end of the curler. Rounded curler rubbers are less likely to mark and break hair than are the flat ones.

Selecting curler size

When selecting curler size, two things must be considered:

l amount of curl desired

l physical characteristics of the hair.

Curl desired: The amount of wave, curl, or body needed is determined between you and your client during the consultation. Your success in creating a style depends primarily on the curler sizes you choose, the number of curlers used, and where the curlers are placed on the head.

Hair characteristics: Of the hair characteristics described earlier, three are important to curler size selection:

l hair length

l hair elasticity

l hair texture.

Suggested hair sectioning and curler size

Although the hair length, elasticity, and texture must be considered in the choice of curlers, the texture should be the determining factor.

Coarse texture, good elasticity

Requires smaller (narrower) sections and larger curlers to permit better placement of curlers for a definite wave pattern.

Medium texture, average elasticity

Medium or average textured hair requires sections that are the same size as the size of the curler.

Fine texture, poor elasticity

Requires smaller sections and curlers wound without any tension on the hair.

9. To maintain better control over the winding and processing, it is advisable to complete the winding of each strand before proceeding to the next one.

10. Test curls should be taken from the curlers closer to the scalp, because the hair in this area is more resistant and might require additional processing.

Figure 5A.37 Locating end tissue part way down for piggy-back wind

Figure 5A.38 Locating first perm rod for piggy-back wind

Figure 5A.39 First rod wound and in place for piggy-back wind

Figure 5A.40 Piggy-back curlers fixed in place

When winding hair, always avoid bulkiness on the rod. Bulkiness prevents the formation of a good curl because the hair cannot conform to the shape of the curler, and the waving lotion and neutraliser cannot penetrate evenly and thoroughly. To ensure a smooth wave formation and to avoid fishhook (buckled) ends, the first part-turn of the curler should be the end papers without any of the hair ends between them.

Piggy-back wind (alternative method)

This technique avoids the distortion of the hair that can at times occur in the area between the two curlers. It does, however, create an elongated curl on the area of the hair nearest the scalp.

1. Locate the end papers at the ends of the hair and wind the ends of the hair with the smaller perm curler.

2. Wind the curler to a mid point of the hair length and then insert a second perm curler.

3. Wind both curlers together to the scalp and secure.

PRELIMINARY (PRE-PERM) TEST CURLS

Preliminary test curls help determine how your client's hair will react to a perm. It is advisable to carry out a test on hair that is tinted, bleached, over-porous, or shows any signs of damage.

Preliminary testing gives you the following additional information:

I Actual processing time needed to achieve optimum curl results.

I Curl results based on the curler size and perm product you have selected.

Procedure

1. Shampoo the hair and towel dry.

2. Following the perm direction, wrap two or three curlers in the most delicate areas of the hair.

3. Wind a coil of cotton wool around the curlers.

4. Apply waving lotion to the wrapped curls, being careful not to allow the waving lotion to come into contact with the unwrapped hair.

5. Set a time and process the hair according to the perm directions.

6. Check the hair frequently.

To check a test curl, unfasten a rod and carefully (remember – the hair is in a softened state) unwind the curl about $1\frac{1}{2}$ turns of the curler. Do not permit the hair to become loose or unwound from the curler completely. Hold the hair firmly by placing a thumb at each end of the curler. Move the curler gently towards the scalp so that the hair falls loosely into the wave pattern. Continue checking the curlers until a firm and definite 'S' is formed. The 'S' reflects the size of the rod used (see Figure 5A.41). Be guided by the manufacturer's directions.

When judging test curls, different hair textures with varying degrees of elasticity will have slightly different 'S' formations. Fine, thin hair is generally softer and has less bulk. The wave ridge might be less defined and more difficult to read. Coarse, thick hair has better elasticity and seems to reinforce itself, falling into the wave pattern more readily. The wave ridge will be stronger and better defined. Long hair may produce a wider scalp wave than short hair, because larger curlers are used and the diameter of the wave widens towards the scalp.

When the optimum curl has been formed, rinse the curls with warm water, blot the curls thoroughly, apply, process and rinse the neutraliser according to the perm directions and gently dry these test curls. Evaluate the curl results. If the hair is over processed (see below), do not perm the rest of the hair until it is in better condition. If the test curl results are good, proceed with the perm, but do not re-perm these preliminary test curls.

Overprocessing

Any lotion that can properly process the hair can also overprocess it, causing dryness, frizziness, or hair damage. Overprocessed hair is easily detected. It cannot be combed into a suitable wave pattern, because the elasticity of the hair has been excessively damaged, and the hair feels harsh after being dried. Reconditioning treatments should begin immediately.

Causes of over processing are:

I Lotion left on the hair too long.

I Improperly judged pre-perm hair analysis and/or waving lotion that was too strong.

I Test curls were not made frequently enough or were judged improperly.

HEALTH AND SAFETY: When applying perm lotion you should wear protective gloves or apply barrier cream to your hands.

Figure 5A.41 Unwinding hair carefully, without pushing or pulling

Figure 5A.42 a Good results;
b Underprocessed curl;
c Overprocessed curl;
d Porous ends;
e Improper winding.

Underprocessing

Underprocessing is caused by insufficient processing time of the waving lotion. After perming, underprocessed hair has a limp or weak wave formation. The ridges are not well defined, and the hair retains little or no wave formation. Typically, after a few shampooings, the hair will have no curl pattern at all (see Figure 5A.42).

Underprocessed hair, even if there is no curl, has been chemically treated. If, in your professional judgement, you decide the hair can be re-permed, condition it first, choose a milder lotion, and test the curls frequently.

IMPORTANT SAFETY PRECAUTIONS

Remember that the lotions used for perming contain chemically active ingredients and therefore must be used carefully to avoid injury to you and your client. The following precautions should always be taken:

I Protect your client's clothing with a plastic shampoo cape.

I Ask your client to remove glasses, earrings, and necklaces to prevent damage.

I Do not give a perm to a client who has experienced an allergic reaction to a previous perm.

I Do not save any opened, unused waving lotion or neutraliser. These lotions can change in strength and effectiveness if not used within a few hours of opening the container.

I Do not dilute or add anything to the waving lotion or neutraliser unless the product directions tell you to do so.

I Keep waving lotion out of eyes and away from the skin. If waving lotion contacts these areas, rinse thoroughly with cool, clean water.

I Do not perm and apply hair colour to a client on the same day. Perm the hair first, wait one week, then apply hair colour. There are products available today which combine perming and colouring within the one process.

PERMING TECHNIQUES

Before you begin perming, make sure you have all the necessary materials at hand. Good organisation and planning will help to develop precision and speed in completing a perm. At the perming station the following equipment should be laid out in an organised, easily accessible fashion:

I perm product

I client's record card

I towels

I curlers (organised by size)

I plastic hair clips and pins

I end papers

I pin tail comb

I cotton wool

I protective gloves

I perm lotion applicator.

Some alkaline perm product directions call for water winding, some are lotion wound, and others require pre-wind lotions. Some wave lotions come in two parts that must be mixed just prior to use. Some need dryer

TIP: Always read and follow the manufacturer's directions carefully.

heat. (Note: the dryer should be pre-heated.) Some perms require that a plastic cap be placed over the curlers during the processing, others do not. Considering all the variables, it is not a good idea to trust your memory. Make it a practice to check the printed directions that accompany every perm each time you give a perm.

Partial perming

Perming only a section of a whole head of hair is called partial perming. Partial perming can be used on:

1. clients (male and female) who have long hair on the top and crown and very short, tapered sides and nape

2. clients who need volume and lift only in certain areas

3. designs that require curl support in the nape area but a smooth, sleek surface.

Partial perming uses the same techniques and wrapping patterns that have already been described. There are a few additional considerations:

1. When you are winding the hair and reach the area that will be left unpermed, go to the next larger curler size so that the curl pattern of the permed hair will blend into the unpermed hair.

2. After wrapping the area to be permed, place a coil of moist cotton wool around the wrapped curlers as well as around the entire hairline.

3. Before applying the waving lotion, apply a heavy, creamy conditioner to the sections that **will not** be permed to protect this hair from the effects of the waving lotion (waving lotion softens and straightens unwrapped hair).

Applying perming lotion

The technique used in applying perming lotion will vary depending on a number of considerations.

Styles of application

Pre-saturation

May be used when perming strong straight hair. By applying the lotion to all of the hair before commencing winding, the hair begins to soften uniformly, and offers less resistance to winding.

Pre-damping

Wetting the hair with perm lotion as you wind. This enables more resistant areas, if wound first, to begin to soften before the less resistant, therefore producing an even curl development throughout the hair. This method may also be used when perming hair using winding patterns to which it may be difficult to apply the perm lotion after winding. In some cases a mild lotion strength may be used as a winding lotion, followed by a stronger lotion, post-damping. This is often used when perming hair with differing rates of porosity along the hair's length.

Post-damping

The hair is water wound, and then the lotion is applied after the wind is completed. This gives time for the winding process to take place. Care must be taken to ensure that lotion is applied to all wound curlers.

After shampooing, shaping, and wrapping the hair, place a coil or band of moist cotton wool around the entire hairline. To prevent skin irritation and for added protection, apply a barrier cream to skin around the hairline before applying the cotton wool band. This safety precaution prevents waving lotion from coming into contact with the skin and possibly causing

HEALTH AND SAFETY: Whenever winding with perm lotion, either pre-saturation or pre-damping, wear protective gloves to protect your skin.

87

Figure 5A.43 Applying perm lotion to wound hair

Figure 5A.44 Processing timer

irritation. If lotion is applied accurately there should be a minimum of dripping, but the cotton wool assures your client's comfort and safety. After the waving lotion has been applied, remove the cotton wool, gently pat the skin with water-soaked cotton wool, and replace with fresh.

Unless otherwise specified in the product instruction, apply waving lotion with care to the wound hair. Systematically apply lotion to each curler, in turn, using an applicator bottle. Run the nozzle along the top of the curler, releasing lotion onto the hair. Avoid allowing lotion to flood onto the scalp. Coverage will be assured by making three applications to the entire head, a little at a time. Remember, dry hair will not absorb moisture easily. By gradually adding lotion to the hair, it will be more readily absorbed ensuring thorough distribution and coverage (see Figure 5A.43).

Processing time

Processing time is the length of time required for the hair strands to absorb the waving lotion (softening). It depends on the hair type (porosity, elasticity, length, density, texture, and overall condition) and the specific perm you are using. Again, follow the manufacturer's directions closely. It is usually safe to anticipate that the processing time will be less than suggested by the manufacturer or a client's previous record card. Some perms have stop-action processing so that all you have to do is set a timer (see Figure 5A.44). Some perms give you a general timetable to follow and require that you do a test curl during processing. It is very important to accurately time the perm process to help prevent over- or underprocessing.

The ability of the hair to absorb moisture may vary from time to time in the same individual, even when the same lotions and procedures are used. A record of the previous processing time is desirable, but should be used only as a guide.

It is sometimes necessary to saturate all the curlers a second time during processing. This might be due to:

- evaporation of the lotion or dryness of the hair
- hair poorly saturated by the hairstylist
- no wave development after the maximum time indicated by the manufacturer
- improper selection of solution strength for the client's hair
- failure to follow the manufacturer's directions for a specific formula.

A reapplication of the lotion will hasten processing. Watch the wave development closely. Negligence can result in hair damage.

Most manufacturers provide instructions with their product. Here are some you will encounter:

- 'Process at room temperature'. Make sure that your client is not sitting in a draught or too close to a heater. A room that is cool slows down the processing.
- 'Place a plastic cap over the wrapped curlers'. Be sure that the plastic cap covers all the curlers and that the cap is airtight. Secure the cap with a non-metallic clip. The cap holds in scalp heat. If it is too loose or if all the rods are not covered, processing might take longer A dry towel placed over the plastic cap will increase the effect and will reduce the influence of blasts of warm or cold air on parts of the head (producing uneven development).
- 'Use a preheated dryer'. Turn the hood dryer to a high setting and medium air flow. Allow the dryer to warm up for approximately 5 minutes before placing your client under the dryer. Cover the wound curlers with a plastic cap secured in place, locate the hood to enclose all

of the curlers and reduce the heat to a medium setting. (Note: Dryer filters should be cleaned frequently so that optimum heat and airflow will remain constant.) Take care not to overprocess the hair, in particular porous hair.

l 'Use an accelerator'. This may be used to aid the process of the perm. The curlers are not usually covered with a plastic cap. The accelerator must be located correctly and evenly around the head. Using the correct heat setting process, taking care not to allow the hair to become dry. In some cases these machines are programmable to particular lotions and hair types. Having located a sensor on the hair it will regulate the processing.

Testing curls during processing

Optimum curl development occurs only once during the processing time. The ability to read a test curl 'S' formation and recognise proper wave development will help you avoid overprocessing and underprocessing. Three test curls should be taken: in the nape, on top of the head and on the side of the head. These three locations will allow you to judge the progress of curl development on the most resistant and the least resistant areas of the head. Follow the procedure for unwinding the curler and checking the 'S'-pattern formation described in the preliminary (pre-perm) test curl section on pages 85–86 (see Figure 5A.45).

Water rinsing

Figure 5A.45 Properly processed strand opens up into 'S' formation

❶

Rinsing the waving lotion from the hair is extremely important. Any lotion left in the hair can cause poor perm results. When your test curl indicates that the optimum curl has been achieved, remove the cotton wool from around the hairline. Rinse the hair thoroughly with a moderate force of warm water. The manufacturer's perm directions will indicate for how long you should rinse – usually 3 to 5 minutes. Always set your timer for the exact time. Remember, you are rinsing the lotion out of the internal hair structure, not merely off the surface. Make sure that all curlers are thoroughly rinsed. Pay special attention to the curlers at the nape of the neck. They are a little difficult to reach, but they must be rinsed as well as all the other curlers. Long hair and thick hair usually require the maximum rinsing time (5 minutes) to make sure that all lotion has been removed from all hair wrapped around the curlers. Indicator papers are available which, when pressed to the hair, will indicate if any perm lotion remains in the hair.

Undesirable effects of improper or incomplete rinsing include:

l Early curl relaxation. Even if the perm has been processed correctly, any waving lotion left in the hair can interfere with the action of the neutraliser. If the neutraliser is not able to properly rebond the hair, the curl will be weak or will not last very long.

l Lightening of hair colour (natural or tint). Rinsing helps reduce the pH of the hair and helps to close the cuticle layer. If the hair is not rinsed properly, the hydrogen peroxide in the neutraliser can react with waving lotion left in the hair and cause the hair colour to lighten. This lightening effect is usually seen on the hair ends.

l Residual perm odour. If any waving lotion is left in the hair, it will become trapped inside the hair when the neutraliser is applied. This is especially true of acid-balanced perms. Unpleasant odours may be evident each time the hair gets wet or damp.

be done with the first and second fingers or with the handle of a tail comb. In either case, you must exercise great care not to scratch the scalp. Such scratches may become seriously infected when aggravated by the chemicals in the relaxer (see Figure 5B.2).

Figure 5B.1 Relaxer record

———————————— **RELAXER RECORD** ————————————

Name ....Tel. ....

Address ....

....

DESCRIPTION OF HAIR

Form	Length	Texture		Porosity	
☐ wavy	☐ short	☐ coarse	☐ soft	☐ very porous	☐ less porous
☐ curly	☐ medium	☐ medium	☐ silky	☐ moderately porous	☐ least porous
☐ extra-curly	☐ long	☐ fine	☐ wiry		
				☐ normal	☐ resistant

Condition

☐ virgin	☐ retouched	☐ dry	☐ oily	☐ lightened

Tinted with...

Previously relaxed with (name of relaxer) ....

☐ Original sample of hair enclosed   ☐ not enclosed

TYPE OF RELAXER OR STRAIGHTENER

☐ whole head   ☐ retouch

☐ retouch ....strength ....☐ straightener ....strength ....

Results

☐ good	☐ poor	☐ sample of relaxed hair enclosed	☐ not enclosed

Date   Operator   Date   Operator

....

....

....

Figure 5B.2 Examining the scalp

If your client has scalp eruptions or abrasions, do not apply the chemical hair relaxer until the scalp is healthy. If the hair is not in a healthy condition, prescribe a series of conditioning treatments to return it to a more normal condition. Then you may give a strand test.

Strand tests

To help you estimate the results you may expect to get from chemical relaxing, it is advisable to test the hair for porosity and elasticity. This can be done using one of the following strand tests:

Finger test

A finger test determines the degree of porosity of the hair. Grasp a strand of hair and run it between the thumb and first finger of the right hand, from the end towards the scalp. If it ruffles or feels bumpy, the hair is porous and can absorb moisture.

Pull test

This test determines the degree of elasticity in the hair. Normally, dry, curly hair will stretch by about 20% of its normal length without breaking. Grasp half a dozen strands from the crown area and pull them gently. If the hair appears to stretch, it has elasticity and can withstand the relaxer. If not, conditioning treatments are recommended prior to a chemical relaxing treatment.

Relaxer test

Application of the relaxer to a hair strand will indicate the reaction of the relaxer on the hair. Take a small section of hair from the crown or another area where the hair is wiry and resistant. Pull it through a slit in a piece of aluminium foil placed as close to the scalp as possible. Apply relaxer to the strand in the same manner as you would apply it to the entire head. Process the strand until it is sufficiently relaxed, checking the strand every 3 to 5 minutes. Make careful notes of timing, the smoothing required, and the hair strength. Shampoo the relaxer from the strand only, towel dry, and cover with protective cream to avoid damage during the relaxing service. If breakage has occurred, you should do another strand test using a milder solution (see Figure 5B.3).

CHEMICAL HAIR RELAXING PROCESS (WITH SODIUM HYDROXIDE)

The procedure outlined below is based primarily on products containing sodium hydroxide. For this or any other kind of product, follow the manufacturer's directions.

Figure 5B.3 Relaxer strand test

Equipment, implements, and materials		
Chemical relaxer	Protective gloves	Absorbent cotton wool
Conditioner	Neutraliser or neutralising shampoo	Towels
Rollers	Shampoo and cream rinse	Comb and brush
Spatula	Clips	End papers
Protective base	Timer	Setting lotion
Conditioner - filler	Record card	

Preparation

1. Select and arrange the required equipment, implements, and materials.
2. Wash and dry your hands.
3. Seat your client comfortably. Remove earrings and neck jewellery; adjust towel and shampoo cape.
4. Examine and evaluate the scalp and hair.
5. Give a strand test and check results.
6. Do not shampoo hair. (Hair ends may be trimmed after application of hair relaxer.)
7. Check the client's record card.

Procedure

1. Part hair into four or five sections (see Figures 5B.4 and 5B.5).
2. Dry the hair. If moisture or perspiration is present on the scalp because of excessive heat or humidity, place your client under a cool dryer for several minutes.
3. Apply protective base. Manufacturers recommend the use of a protective base to protect the scalp from the strong chemicals in the relaxer. To apply it properly, subdivide each of the four or five major sections into 1 to 2 cm partings, to permit thorough scalp coverage (see Figure 5B.6).

Apply the base freely to the entire scalp with your fingers. The hairline around the forehead, nape of the neck, and area over and around the ears must be completely covered. Complete coverage is important to protect the scalp and hairline from irritation.

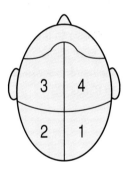

Figure 5B.4 Part hair into four sections

Figure 5B.5 Part hair into five sections; three sections in front area, two sections in back area

Figure 5B.6 Applying protective base

TIP: When using a 'no-base' relaxer, a protective base is not necessary. It is recommended that a protective cream be used on the hairline and around the ears.

HEALTH AND SAFETY: Avoid the use of heat, which will open the pores of the scalp and cause irritation or injury to the client's scalp. Protective gloves must be worn by the hairdresser to prevent damage to hands.

Applying the conditioner-filler

In many cases a conditioner-filler is required before the chemical relaxer can be used. The conditioner-filler, usually a protein polymer product, is applied to the entire head of hair when dry. It protects over-porous or slightly damaged hair from being over-processed on any part of the hair shaft. It evens out the porosity of the hair shaft, and permits uniform distribution and action of the chemical relaxer.

To give the full benefit of the conditioner-filler, rub it gently onto the hair from the scalp to the hair ends, using either the hands or a comb. Then towel dry the hair or use a cool dryer to completely dry the hair.

Applying the relaxer

Divide the head into four or five sections, in the same manner as for the application of the protective base.

The processing cream is applied last to the scalp area and hair ends. The body heat will speed up the processing action at the scalp. The hair is more porous at the ends and may be damaged. In both these areas, less processing time is required, and, therefore, the relaxer is applied last to these parts.

There are three methods in general use for the application of the chemical hair relaxer: the comb method, the brush method, and the finger method.

Comb method

Remove a quantity of relaxing cream from the tub, using a spatula. Beginning in the back right section of the head, carefully part off 0.5 cm to 1 cm of hair, depending on its thickness and curliness. Apply the relaxer with the back of the comb, starting 0.5 cm to 1 cm from the scalp, and spread to within 1 cm of the hair ends. First apply the relaxer to the top side of the strand (see Figure 5B.7). Then, raise the subsection and apply the relaxer underneath. Gently lay the completed strand up, out of the way (see Figure 5B.8).

Figure 5B.7 Applying relaxer on top of strand

Figure 5B.8 Applying relaxer underneath strand

Complete the right back area and, moving in a clockwise direction, cover each section of the head in the same manner. Then, go back over the head in the same order, applying additional relaxing cream if necessary, and spreading the relaxer close to the scalp and up to the hair ends. Avoid excessive pressure or stretching of the hair.

Smoothing the cream through the hair not only spreads the cream, but also stretches the hair gently into a straight position.

An alternative technique is to begin application at the nape, approximately 2 cm from the hairline, and continue towards the crown. The last place to apply relaxer is at the hairline. Be guided by the manufacturer's instructions.

Brush or finger method

The brush or finger method of applying the relaxer to the hair is the same as the comb method, except that the brush or fingers and palms are used instead of the back of the comb.

Periodic strand testing

While spreading the relaxer, inspect its action by stretching the strands to see how fast the natural curls are being removed. Another method of testing is to press the strand to the scalp using the back of the comb or your finger. Examine the strand after your finger is removed. If it lies smoothly, the strand is sufficiently relaxed; if the strand revert or 'beads' back away from the scalp, continue processing.

Rinsing out the relaxer

When the hair has been sufficiently straightened, rinse the relaxer out rapidly and thoroughly. The water must be warm, not hot (see Figure 5B.9). If the water is too hot, it may burn the client and cause discomfort because of the very sensitive condition of the scalp. If the water is too cold, it will not stop the processing action. The direct force of the rinse water should be used to remove the relaxer and avoid tangling the hair. Part hair with fingers to make sure no traces of the relaxer remain. Unless the relaxer is completely removed, its chemical action continues on the hair. The stream of water should be directed from the scalp to the hair ends.

Shampooing/neutralising

When the hair is thoroughly rinsed, neutralise the hair as directed by the manufacturer's directions. Most manufacturers provide a neutralising shampoo which is applied to the hair after rinsing. Others prescribe the use of a non-alkaline or a cream shampoo followed by a neutraliser.

Gently work the shampoo into the hair. Use care to avoid tangling the hair or breaking any fragile ends. Manipulate the shampoo by working with the fingers underneath the hair, not on top. Rinse with warm water, making sure to keep the hair straight. Repeat the shampoo until the hair lathers well and all the relaxer is removed (see Figure 5B.10).

After shampooing, completely saturate the hair with the neutraliser if it is required by the manufacturer. Beginning at the nape, and comb carefully with a wide-toothed comb, working upward towards the forehead. Use the comb to:

I keep the hair straight

I ensure complete saturation with the neutraliser

I remove any tangles without pulling.

Time the neutraliser as directed and rinse thoroughly. Towel blot gently. Condition hair as necessary and proceed with styling. Discard used materials. Clean and sterilise equipment. Wash and dry your hands. Complete the record of all timings and treatments during the service, and file the record card.

Applying the conditioner

Many manufacturers recommend that you apply a conditioner before setting the hair, to offset the harshness of the sodium hydroxide in the relaxer and to help restore some of the natural oils to the scalp and hair.

Two types of conditioners are available: cream-type and protein-type.

HEALTH AND SAFETY: Wear protective gloves.

Figure 5B.9 Rinsing out relaxer

HEALTH AND SAFETY: Do not get relaxer or rinse water into the eyes or on unprotected skin. If the relaxer or rinse water gets into the client's eyes, wash it out immediately and refer the client to a doctor without delay.

Figure 5B.10 Shampooing the hair

NOTE: Different products used for relaxing require different methods. Always follow the manufacturer's directions.

Styling lotions should be suggested to suit the method of styling, as well as setting lotions which contain protein and will strengthen the hair. For curly looks, curl activators may be used to maintain the level of moisture and oil in the hair.

FURTHER STUDY

I Look on the packages of straightening products to see the range of product strengths available for use in the salon and at home.

I Manufacturer's directions for use vary; look at a range of instruction leaflets to see the range of variations.

I Find out the range of after-care products available for the care of hair which has been straightened and relaxed.

Review questions

1. Name two chemicals often used in chemical hair relaxing products.

2. What does the term 'base' mean in relation to hair relaxation processes?

3. How may the client's hairline and face be protected during these chemical processes?

4. What are the three main stages of the chemical hair relaxation process?

5. What is a strand test used for?

6. How should hairdressers protect themselves when working with relaxing/straightening substances?

7. How close to the scalp should straightener products be applied?

8. What are the main stages of a two-step perm?

9. What is meant by 'over-directing' when curler winding?

10. What tension should be used when winding hair during a 'two-step perm'?

6 Hair colouring

This chapter will give you the essential knowledge necessary for you to understand the hair colouring process. It will guide you in hair colour and product selection as well as in the application techniques available to the professional hair colourist and their suitability.

CONTENTS

INTRODUCTION

Hairdressing is a career that offers you opportunities to develop your creative talents in many different ways. One of the most exciting and challenging areas of creativity in your career as a professional hair stylist will be colouring and lightening.

Hair colouring includes the processes of:

- adding artificial pigment to the natural hair colour
- adding artificial pigment to previously coloured hair
- adding artificial pigment to pre-lightened hair
- lightening natural pigment and adding artificial pigment in one step.

(The terms 'tinting' and 'colouring' are used interchangeably in this text.)

Hair lightening involves the diffusing of the natural pigment or artificial colour from the hair. Hair lightening involves the process of:

- lightening the natural pigment to prepare the hair for the final colour (pre-lightening)
- lightening the natural or artificial pigment to the desired colour (lightening)
- lightening the natural or artificial pigment for corrective colouring
- lightening the natural or artificial pigment in selected areas (highlighting).

What the expert says

Hair colouring is one of those professional services that separate the enthusiastic amateur from the skilled professional. Hair colour products are ever increasingly available to the consumer via the high street retail outlets, but the vital ingredient of professional advice and technical service can only come from the experienced and skilled hairdresser. As a professional hairdresser you must capitalise on this skill. The chemical services are profitable sources of salon income and colouring represents repeat business. The client who has tinted or lightened hair usually returns for retouching at regular intervals. Satisfactory service and trust in their colourist encourage clients to remain loyal to the same salon and will in all probability mean that they use additional services that the salon offers.

Your success as a colourist depends only on the time and energy you are prepared to give to the continuous study and practice of your hair colouring skills. As you expand your skills and gain confidence, you may choose to specialise in hair colouring services, similar to medical professionals who practise in and develop one area of expertise. Colourists have a major role to play in the success of any hairdressing business. Their skill and expertise will enhance the work of the hair stylist and satisfy the client's need. There is the potential for the skilled colourist to establish a reputation for their own skills in guiding the client towards the most suitable colour choice and in using the most appropriate technique to apply the colouration to the hair. Colourists have the opportunity to develop their own formulations and techniques, using the product manufacturer's guidance and their own skill and experience to vary techniques to produce bespoke colouring for their clients.

The styling revolution

Thanks to the styling revolution in the 1960s and 1970s, there are many stylists who have mastered hair cutting or perming, and concentrate their energies solely on these frequently requested services. Add colour to a great haircut and perfect texture, and you've got a powerful attention-getting combination. Specialist hair colourists are less common than cutters, and their skills are in increasingly high demand due to renewed publicity and popularity.

Keeping up to date

The colouring houses are always willing to promote and inform the professional about their products. Use this facility to develop your skill and to maintain the currency of your product knowledge and your application technique skills. The manufacturers are generally very keen to inform and update the hairdresser.

Help and advice

Most hair colouring houses have a telephone help line to offer professional advice and guidance in the use of their products. Should you experience problems in the use of their products make use of this facility.

As a professional hair colourist you should ensure that you constantly update your skills and make yourself aware of what is available so that you can advise both the business and your clientele of the most recent developments and technology.

HAIR COLOUR CONSULTATION

As with all facets of the hairdresser's role, consultation with the client is of crucial importance.

Reasons clients colour their hair

There are five main reasons why clients wish to colour their hair: to boost self-image, to keep up to date with fashion, for artistic reasons, in reaction to greying and to correct faults in their current colour. These can be sub-divided as follows.

Self-image boost

l To alleviate boredom or depression.

l To promote a more professional appearance.

Fashion

l To subtly enhance their existing hair colour.

l To create a fashion statement or follow a trend which expresses their personality.

Artistic

l To accentuate their hairstyle design, making it look more finished.

l To enhance or minimise their features, using colour to create illusions.

Greying

l To conceal premature greying.

l To keep and enhance their natural white or grey and eliminate yellow.

Corrective

l To eliminate the damaged look of sun-lightened hair ends.

l To remove the unsightly cast of chlorine or minerals caused by their water.

l To improve upon the results of previous colour experimentation.

Almost everyone at one time or another has considered doing something a little different with their hair. Our potential clients may have already done

> **TIP:** Hair stylists willing to develop their colouring skills and expertise can serve the needs of a huge and growing market.

Figure 6.1 There are many reasons clients choose to colour their hair. To cover grey is one

Figure 6.2 Hair colouring is a popular service for the male clientele today

some experimentation at home or in another salon by changing their haircut or style, their hair texture by perming, or their hair's natural colour.

With the emergence and availability of non-professional products that your clients can buy, why should they come to you, a professional colourist, for advice and service? And who are the 'typical' hair colouring clients today? (see Figure 6.1).

Typical clients

Hair colouring offers a wide variety of choices and therefore attracts the attention and interest of anyone who wants to look good and feel better. Gone are the stereotypes of the obviously tinted client – the damaged hair, the flat or unnatural appearance. Typical clients may want to cover or enhance their grey; they may be teenagers, women, and men who enjoy frequent fashion changes; they are often clients currently unhappy with their natural colour or who want to improve the shine and texture of their hair; they may be current hair colouring clients who come in for their retouch applications and a little relaxation time to themselves. Even the male clientele for hair colour is growing rapidly and is expected to be the fastest growing category of hair colouring client this decade (see Figure 6.2).

As a trained professional hair colourist, you will have access to professional-only products which far surpass the ones your clients can purchase in selection, performance, and stability. You will know which colours look best on your clients, which products and application techniques will best achieve the desired look, how to choose these products and customise them to fit hair conditions at different times of year, and how hair colouring and lightening products will react on clients' hair. The key to your success in hair colouring is communication.

With continuously developing technology and the latest advancements in hair colour education, hair colouring manufacturers are moving to standardise terminology in order to simplify learning and provide greater assistance to colourists.

The colourist's role in client communication

Observe

Simple observation gives you a chance to use your training and analyse client's needs. Your eyes are your primary information-gathering tools. The following is a list of factors about hair that influence colour choice. With time and practice, you will notice certain physical characteristics relevant to hair colour selection when you first see a client. These are items you will need to note when observing clients prior to hair colouring service:

I colour level

I colour tone

I eye colour

I skin tone

I length

I porosity

I density

I texture

I shape

I percentage of grey.

Each of these will be described in detail as we go through a typical hair colour consultation.

The consultation is a time when your greeting and appearance should be at their most impressive. The greeting establishes your credibility and trustworthiness.

You only have one chance to make a first impression on your clients, so make it a good one. You alone are responsible for the image you project. Make sure your clients and potential clients see you as you want them to. Establish and maintain eye contact, make clients comfortable, and listen.

Listen

Listening allows you to find out how clients view their needs. The finest formulation combined with the most talented application will still result in colour failure if clients are dissatisfied.

Despite all the activity in a busy salon, your client's thoughts are centred mainly on their own concerns. So, naturally, all clients expect to be treated with courtesy and attention. The hair stylist who recognises this fact and gives clients respect, courtesy, and attention will win their confidence. And, when this hair stylist sincerely recommends a hair colour service, clients are likely to listen carefully and seriously consider the recommendation.

Make suggestions

To recommend a hair colour service with sincerity means to suggest a colour only when you honestly believe that your client would be happier and more attractive with the colour service. You must be attentive to your clients' needs by listening closely, by being genuinely interested, and by treating every client as you would like to be treated yourself in the same situation. In doing so, you can be confident that your choice will reflect and meet any client's needs, improve your client's appearance, and enhance your reputation as a colourist (see Figure 6.3).

Explain time and monetary investment involved

At the completion of your consultation, you should have an agreement with your clients as to what is needed, how long it will take, and how much it will cost.

Determine a solution to fulfil the client's needs

Hair colouring is a wonderful service, and can make a tremendous difference to your client. Whether you choose a subtle change or something quite dramatic, the opportunity to create is greatly enhanced by being able to offer a hair colour service.

In the following pages, you will learn how to analyse your client's needs and choose and perform a hair colour service. There are many choices and considerations. Hair colouring is an art, something to be learned over time, not simply by reading books. The people who walk into your salon to become your clients bring not only their hair, but their likes and dislikes, their hopes and dreams – a whole wealth of experiences in which you can share. Take your time, look carefully, listen well, and offer the gift of your art.

Hair colour consultation: the environment

The consultation is one of the most important steps in the hair colouring service. But first there are other important elements to consider that will allow you to 'set the stage' for your consultation success.

Setting the stage: the proper environment

Adequate lighting

Light, and how it plays with hair colour, is of prime importance to the hair colourist. Bright natural light makes hair colour appear different than does dim light. Electric lights of varying intensities and hues also alter the eye's perception of colour.

TIP: Your professional appearance, confident manner and use of professional industry terminology will establish you as an authority in your client's eyes.

Figure 6.3 Good communication is essential when discussing a hair colouring service with a client

Perform the consultation in a well-lit room, preferably with natural lighting. If this is not possible, arrange the lighting so that there is incandescent light in front of the client (around the mirrors) and fluorescent behind the colourist (ceiling fixtures).

Incandescent lighting alone will make the hair and skin tones appear warmer than they truly are; fluorescent lighting alone has a cool cast and will give the skin and hair a pale and unnatural 'grey' appearance. Always remember to consider the lighting in which your clients will see themselves; a beautifully subtle highlight in natural sunlight may disappear under office lighting. Conversely, a strong, attractive colour in your salon lighting could become neon-looking in the sunlight.

The best mix of lighting for hair colour is to use full-spectrum white fluorescent tubes, or consider adding track lighting spot lights (incandescent) to existing fluorescent lighting in most buildings.

Colour of consultation area

Privacy and good lighting are important. Ideally, a separate room (or area) in the salon should be reserved specifically for consultations. If possible, the walls should be white or neutral, and neutral gowning should be used to conceal your client's street clothes, especially if they are strong colours that may influence your perception of the clients' hair and skin tonality.

Gathering and using colour consultation tools

In your consultation room or area, you will keep all of your professional hair colouring consultation tools – items that will make communication with your clients go smoothly. Keep a hair colour portfolio of your work or magazines and picture books with different hair colouring levels, tones, intensities, and application techniques, so clients can show you the general hair colour they have in mind. Ink colours on the page will not exactly match coloured pigments in hair, but if you tell your clients this you will both still be able to use these tools as a guide to understanding the desired colour.

Manufacturers' paper colour charts and hair colour swatches, although showing colour on white paper or on white hair, will at least give you an idea of the client's wishes. After all, your idea of red and a client's idea of red may be different – as different as strawberry blonde and burgundy. Manufacturers also make available to colourists their natural colour swatches, to help you judge the natural hair colour depth or level based on their colour product's system (see Figure 6.4). These are usually part of the product shade chart.

A client record card (see Figure 6.5) will be necessary to transfer your hair analysis, testing, and consultation information into a permanent file, whether paper based or computerised. You will also want to gather together your materials for strand and predisposition tests, which will be performed prior to each service in this chapter.

Pre-colour testing
Strand test to confirm colour selection

Before applying a tint, conduct a preliminary strand test to confirm your selection. You will learn the following information:

l whether the proper colour selection was made

l timing needed to achieve the desired results

l whether further preconditioning treatments are needed

l whether it is necessary to apply a filler (pre-pigmentation).

Figure 6.4 Hair colourist

TIP: Computerised multi-media style selection systems may be used to illustrate to your client the effects of differing hair colour upon their hairstyle.

Mr/Mrs/Ms Surname First names	Address Post Code Tel. no.			
Date of skin test	Result	Hair type/colour/%grey		
Date	Product	Oxidant	Notes	Cost

Figure 6.5 Client record card

Strand test procedure

1. Mix a small amount of the colour, intended for use, with peroxide according to the manufacturer's directions, using plastic measuring spoons to ensure accuracy of proportions (see Figure 6.6).

2. Apply mixture to a 0.125 cm section, usually in the crown area of the head. (Remember to test each area where the hair colour varies. More than one formula may be necessary to achieve even results.)

3. Separate the strand from the rest of the hair using foil or plastic film. Process with or without heat according to the manufacturer's directions, keeping careful records of timing on the client's record card (see Figure 6.7).

4. Rinse the strand, shampoo, towel dry, and examine results (see Figure 6.8). Adjust the formula, timing, or preconditioning as necessary and proceed with tinting on the entire head.

Figure 6.6 Mix colour with peroxide

Figure 6.7 Apply mixture to strand   Figure 6.8 Examine results

5. If results are unsatisfactory, adjust the formula and repeat the process on a new test strand.

Predisposition test to check for client sensitivity

Allergy to aniline derivative tints is unpredictable. Some clients may be sensitive, and others may develop a sensitivity after years of use. To identify an allergic client, a patch, or predisposition test should be given 24 to 48 hours prior to each application of an aniline tint or toner. The tint used for the skin test must be the same formula as that used for the hair colouring service.

Predisposition test procedure

1. Select the test area – behind one ear extending into the hairline or at the inside bend of the elbow (near a pulse point).

2. Using a mild unperfumed soap, cleanse an area about the size of a one pence piece (see Figure 6.9).

3. Dry the area.

4. Prepare the test solution according to the manufacturer's directions (see Figure 6.10).

5. Apply to test area with a sterile cotton wool bud or the end of a clean tint brush. Tell your client what to do should a reaction occur. Your client should remove the patch test and, should the symptoms continue, should consult their medical practitioner. They should also inform you of this occurrence.

6. Leave the area undisturbed for 24 to 48 hours.

TIP: It is important that the hair has received all pre-treatments necessary according to your analysis before the strand test is given, so that results will be accurate.

HEALTH AND SAFETY: A predisposition test must be given before colouring the hair with an aniline derivative product. Operator dermatitis, although rare, involves the same types of reactions as the client can experience. Since the colourist's hands are in water and contact chemical solutions repeatedly throughout an average day, it is important to take proper precautions. You should protect yourself from allergic reactions by wearing protective gloves until the product is completely removed from the client's hair.

Figure 6.9 Clean patch test area

Figure 6.10 Mix tint and peroxide

7. Examine the test area.

8. Note the results on the client's record card.

A *negative* skin reaction will show no sign of inflammation or skin irritation, and colour may safely be applied. If the skin test is *positive*, you will see any or a number of the following: redness, swelling, burning, itching, or blisters. A client with these symptoms is allergic, and should under no circumstance receive the colour service for which the test was performed. Application in this instance could result in a serious reaction for the client, and a professional negligence claim for the hair colourist.

The patch test is also known as an allergy test, a predisposition test or a Sabouraud-Rousseau test.

Client record card

Always record the consultation on the client's record card. It is important to keep an accurate record so that successful services can be repeated and any difficulties encountered in one service may be avoided in the next. A complete record should be kept, containing all analysis notes, strand test and whole head results, timing, costs, and suggestions for the next service.

Analysing the client's hair physiology

No two people are exactly alike, and no two heads of hair are exactly the same. Even an individual client's hair will vary from season to season and from year to year. Every person has a natural hair colour that is either a dark, medium, or light colour, but no two people have exactly the same hair colour. Inside the hair shaft, where you cannot see, the factors that create or affect hair colour are always different from person to person. That is why the same hair colouring formula and procedure will produce a different result for every client (see Figure 6.11).

How hair structure relates to colouring

The hair is a remarkable and resilient fibre. Every hair colour service will affect or be affected by the structure of the hair. Some hair colour products cause a dramatic change in the hair's structure; others affect it very little. When a product significantly changes the hair structure, it usually creates a weaker strand of hair.

Knowing how products affect the structure will allow you to make choices. Your perceptions of what the hair can or cannot tolerate will allow you to be the best judge of what is most appropriate for each client.

Generally every hair on a person's head is composed of three parts: the *cuticle*, the *cortex*, and the *medulla*. The medulla is at the innermost centre of

Figure 6.11 Analysing a client's hair physiology

the hair shaft. The cuticle is the outermost layer of the hair. It is made up of overlapping bands of keratinised protein that is very similar to the protein that makes up our fingernails. It is translucent, allowing diffused light to pass through. The cuticle protects the interior cortex layer of the hair. The shiny appearance of the hair depends on this cuticle layer being smooth and intact. A healthy cuticle contributes 20% to the overall strength of the hair.

The cortex is the second layer of the hair. The natural colour we see in the hair is in this layer. The cortex structure is made up of elongated, fibrous cells bundled together. Melanin pigment granules are scattered between the cortex cells. These granules are embedded in the cortex layer like chips in a chocolate chip biscuit. The strength and elasticity of the hair depend on the cortex layer being intact. A healthy cortex contributes 80% to the overall strength of the hair.

Hair texture is described as the diameter of the individual hair strand. The terms coarse, medium, and fine are used to differentiate between large, medium, and small diameters. Texture has an effect on hair colour because the hair's natural melanin pigment is distributed differently in the different textures. Each diameter also has a different resistance to the changes hair colour chemicals make on the hair shaft (see Figure 6.12).

Fine-textured hair's pigment is grouped more tightly together. Because of this tighter grouping, when you deposit colour, you will have a darker result on fine hair. By the same token, fine hair is less resistant to lightening because there is less structure to resist the chemical. When lightening fine hair, a milder lightener can be used successfully.

Medium-textured hair will have average responses to hair colour products. Note any variations in texture throughout the hair. The front hairline is usually finer in texture than hair further back on the head.

Coarse-textured hair has a more open grouping of hair pigment due the larger diameter hair shaft in which the pigment is located. Because of this open grouping, you will have a slightly lighter result when depositing colour. When lightening the hair, you will encounter greater resistance to the lightener, and a stronger lightening product may be needed.

Porosity is necessary for colour to take properly. Each product you put on the hair requires a different degree of porosity.

Porosity, in simple terms, is the ability of the hair to absorb moisture. Porous hair will accept liquid (hair colour for example) more readily than non-porous hair. Uneven porosity can create problems if even colour results are desired.

As hair grows longer, the ends are subject to frequent shampooing, drying, styling, and environmental influences. There will be visual and textural changes. The cuticle will be slightly abraded (worn away), and the rough hair fibre will loose some of its flexibility, body, and shine. There will also be some variation in colour from strand to strand and even from the scalp area to the mid-lengths. Hair may be lighter and more faded-out towards the ends.

This longer, older hair is described as over-porous, a condition in which hair reaches an undesirable level of porosity. This hair will respond differently to hair colour products from the newer hair closer to the scalp. Those different responses can only be determined by performing a strand test. As a general rule, overporous hair will look duller, flatter and will reflect cooler tones, while the healthier hair will reflect warmer tones.

Occasionally, a client's hair has a cuticle so smooth and compact that you will need to create the proper porosity for the success of your hair colouring service. The hair is considered resistant to the swelling effects of alkalis that

Fine textured hair

Medium textured hair

Coarse textured hair

Figure 6.12 Diameters of various hair strands.

❧ **NOTE: Due to the compact nature of fine hair, depositing colour molecules in the cortex may cause more damage to the structure than it would in coarser hair textures.**❧

113

TIP: Your conversation should be something like: 'This colour (show a picture or swatch) can be achieved by (indicate the type of colour service i.e., weaving, single-process colour, etc.). The cost of this service will be (state cost). How do you feel about this?'

TIP: Remember that your client may not the jargon that you use. Explain the procedure that is about to be used on their hair, in terms which they will understand. This will help to gain their confidence in the process, so they will be more comfortable and therefore more likely to enjoy their visit to your salon.

The time and money involved in committing to a colour service should be spelled out in advance.

This is a time to make direct eye contact with your client and wait for the answer. If the time or cost is objectionable, alter your suggestion. Continue this conversation until you and your client agree to the maintenance schedule you have presented. At this point, you will have an agreement with your client and can begin your service.

Choosing level, tone, and intensity

If necessary you will adjust the hair colour formula for each individual texture or condition. Remember the findings of your analysis, listed on your client's record card. Include the client's current colour in formulating for level, tone, and intensity. Generally speaking, a change of 1 to 2 levels will produce the most natural results. Any tone can be enhanced or subdued to the client's wishes by using the law of colour in selecting your formula. Adjust for grey, porosity, and length. Natural-looking hair colours are a balance between all three primary colours, including the client's contributing pigment and the artificial colour selected.

Selecting the appropriate application technique

After a thorough discussion with your client, you must then choose the method that will achieve the desired effect. Sometimes a combination of application techniques is necessary to first cover grey, then add carefully placed highlights, to make the transition from the lightness of grey to the contrasting darkness of a solid colour. Another example would be the use of a double-process, blending a pastel colour with a cool tone. Whatever you select, make sure the client understands each step of the procedure and the technique necessary to achieve your objective. This will avoid startled looks from clients when they see unexplained things happening to their hair during a procedure.

Using colour keys to find the most flattering colour for the client

Analysing skin and eye colouring

The colour of client's eyes can be a clue as to what their hair colour could be. Eyes are rarely one colour. Usually they are combinations of two or even three colours. Basically there are brown, blue, and green eyes. Look more closely. Brown eyes with olive green, reddish brown, or gold flecks are quite common. Blue eyes may also have flecks of white, gold, or grey. Green eyes can range from grey-green to hazel (with brownish overtones) to yellow-green.

We can categorise eye colour as warm or cool. Warm eye colours contain red, orange, yellow, or gold flecks through the iris of brown, blue, or green.

Warm eye colours are:

l Brown with red, orange, yellow, or gold.

l Blue with yellow or gold.

l Green with reddish brown, orange, yellow, or gold.

People who have warm eye colours can wear warm hair colours. Cool eye colours contain black, grey-brown, grey-green, blue, violet, grey or white flecks through the iris of brown, blue, or green.

Cool eye colours are:

l Brown with black, grey-brown, grey-green, or grey.

l Blue with white, blue, grey, or violet.

l Green with blue or grey.

People with cool eye colours look most attractive with cool or neutral hair colours

The depth of eye colour is another factor in your colour choice. Lighter eyes reflect a lighter pigmentation throughout the client's colouring. A lighter intensity colour choice would be indicated. Medium eyes reflect stronger pigmentation, and more intense colour options are available. Dark eyes reflect the strongest pigmentation. A deeper colour choice is advisable. To choose a colour that will harmonise with the client's natural pigmentation, include the depth of eye colour (light, medium, or dark) in your colour equation.

Skin tone can be broken down into four simple categories: olive, red, golden and neutral. It is easiest to observe the natural skin tone by looking at the skin on the neck, close to the clavicle. Skin on the face and arm is often affected by sun exposure, which masks the skin tone, making it difficult to determine.

Olive skin tones have an underlying tone of grey, green, or yellow. Olive-toned clients look best in cool or neutral colours. If a warm shade is desired, it should be in a darker level.

Red skin tones have an underlying tone of red-brown, red, or blue-red. Red-toned clients look best in cool or neutral colours. Warm colours are not recommended for these clients.

Golden skin tones have an underlying tone of golden brown, gold, or peach. Golden skin tones look best in warm colours. The level chosen would be affected by the client's natural level.

Neutral skin tones are a balance of warm and cool. Neutral skin can have an underlying tone of pink and yellow in combination. You will not observe one predominant underlying skin tone. Generally these skin tones are described as ivory, beige, or brown skin. Neutral skin tones look good in either warm or cool colours.

How does this information indicate a colour choice? The chart on pages 122–3 will help you in your selection. Remember that each person is unique, however, and consult with your trainer or product techician for advice. Gradually, as your skill develops, you will see these items automatically (see Figure 6.20).

Enhancing your client's natural colouring

When working with hair that has not been coloured, you will notice a natural harmony in the hair tone, skin tone, and eye colour tone. Maintaining that natural harmony will give you a pleasing, natural effect. A more avant-garde effect will be achieved by using complementary colour tones. The key to maintaining harmony in colour tone is understanding the *Law of Colour*.

Consider how tones change with maturity. Many clients initially want to return to the colour of their youth. They do not realise that the pigment of their skin is ageing in a process similar to that of the hair. To tint the hair back to the natural colour of their youth creates a severe contrast that can be harsh. Generally, a colour of a similar tone but lighter level will be more flattering.

There will always be clients who break these rules. Many do so with great success. Attractiveness is a quality that incorporates the laws of art and balance, along with the client's personality and self-expression.

TIP: Many clients choose coloured contact lenses to enhance their appearance. This can affect your colour choice. If you are not certain of the client's natural eye colour, always ask.

Colour Key 1

Your natural eye colour

Your natural hair colours and most flattering tints

Your natural skin colours

Makeup and wardrobe colours
for persons in colour Key 1

Colour Key 2

Your natural eye colour

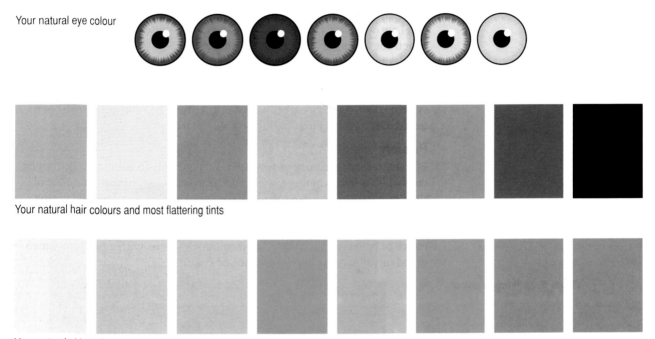

Your natural hair colours and most flattering tints

Your natural skin colours

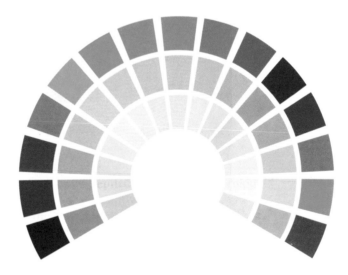

Makeup and wardrobe colours
for persons in colour Key 2

Clean up

1. Discard all disposable supplies and materials.
2. Close containers, wipe them off, and store safely.
3. Clean implements, tint cape, work area, and hands.

Deposit-only (quasi-permanent) hair colour

When semi-permanent colours were first introduced some years ago, clients generally shampooed their hair weekly, making the lasting ability of the semi-permanent colour of the time a satisfactory 4 to 6 weeks. Today, however, with more clients shampooing daily, a colour that lasts 4 to 6 shampoos may be unsatisfactory. For a colour that will act similarly in nature to the semi-permanent colours but will produce a longer-lasting effect, manufacturers have introduced a new category of hair colours called *Deposit-only* or *Quasi-permanent colours*.

Composition and action

The effect of a deposit-only hair colour lies between those of semi-permanent and permanent colour classifications. Deposit-only colours use a form of a catalyst, such as low-volume developers, to gently swell and open the cuticle layer and drive the colour into the cortex. Deposit-only hair colours have small- and medium-sized dye molecules. The small-sized molecules slightly penetrate into the cortex, and the medium-sized dye molecules penetrate the cuticle layers, resulting in a colour that has the gentleness of a semi-permanent colour with the longevity of a permanent hair colour. Deposit-only colours last 4 to 6 weeks, gradually fading from the hair and producing a diffused line of demarcation (see Figure 6.36).

Selecting and formulating a deposit-only (quasi-permanent) colour

Deposit-only hair colours are ideal for grey coverage, to refresh permanent tints, for corrective colouring, lowlighting and for creating quick fashion effects.

By its very nature, a deposit-only hair colour will darken the natural hair colour when applied. Remember, when formulating, that half of your formula will be the client's natural hair colour and half will be the depositing colour you have selected. Since colour on top of colour always appears darker, select a deposit-only colour lighter than the client's natural level if you intend to keep the same amount of depth but add tone.

Since grey hair has no pigment and appears lighter, it is important to consider the grey hair in your formulation of a deposit-only hair colour. As there is no lift, the resulting depth of colour when covering grey may appear too extreme unless you allow for some brightness in your formulation. It is often inadvisable to make grey hair one even shade when colouring with any product, since natural hair colour has different depths and tonalities that give the hair the added life that grey hair is lacking.

It is always better when taking a client from lighter to darker to err on the side of lightness, because a darker tone can easily be used to deepen the colour if necessary. A result which is too dark, on the other hand, will involve corrective procedures to lighten or remove the artificial pigment before re-applying to achieve the desired colour.

Hair previously treated with another colour service will have a greater degree of porosity, which must be considered carefully when formulating and applying a deposit-only hair colour.

Application procedure for deposit-only (quasi-permanent) colours

The application procedure for a deposit-only hair colour is similar to that of a semi-permanent colour, since neither type of colour alters the hair's

Figure 6.36 Action of deposit-only hair colour

TIP: When selecting the formulation for the use of these colours on high percentages of white hair, to avoid over strong or bright results, add base tone to any fashion tone selected.

natural melanin or produces lift. Follow the manufacturer's application and timing guidelines for the product that you have selected.

For successful hair colouring services, the colourist must follow a definite procedure. A system makes for the greatest efficiency, and the most satisfactory results. Without such a plan, the work will take longer, results will be uneven, and mistakes will be made.

Permanent hair colouring

Permanent hair colours are prepared from a variety of materials: vegetables, flowers, herbs, salts of heavy metals, organic and synthetic chemicals. All of these permanent colours fall into one of four classifications: vegetable tints, metallic dyes, compound dyestuffs, or oxidation tints. Practically all permanent hair colouring is done with the use of oxidising penetrating tints which contain aniline derivatives.

These tints penetrate the cuticle of the hair and enter the cortical layer. Here, they are oxidised by the peroxide added into colour pigments. These pigments are distributed throughout the hair shaft much like natural pigment.

Vegetable tints

In the past, before technology brought us the hairdressing industry as we now know it, many vegetable materials such as camomile and henna were used as hair colouring ingredients.

Camomile

Camomile flowers can be ground into a powder and used as a paste. It gives a lighter brighter effect to blonde hair. Shampoos and rinses containing powdered flowers are intended to add a bright yellow colour in the hair. However, camomile's effectiveness is limited to a minimal colour change.

Henna

Henna is the most noteworthy and popular of the vegetable colours and comes from plants grown in moist climates throughout Africa, Arabia, Iran, and the East Indies. The henna leaves are removed before the flowering cycle, dried, and ground into a fine powder. Hot water is added to create a paste.

Henna is a natural product that appeals to the young client and consumers who prefer organic products and avoid synthetics. Its 'natural' qualities appeal to many.

Current technology has brought to the market henna in black, chestnut, and auburn, plus a lightener. These hennas are made of concentrated herbal extracts that have both a cumulative and a semi-permanent effect. The dye coats the hair and is partially removed by shampooing.

The coating action of henna creates a hair strand that becomes thicker, and thus helps to give body to fine, limp hair. Because it makes no structural changes in the hair, it can be used on weak hair without damaging it. Henna fills in a roughened cuticle and holds together split ends to provide a slick, light-reflective surface. This, coupled with the additional warmth, creates hair that shines.

Metallic hair dyes

Metallic hair colours can be recognised by the descriptive terms used by manufacturers in their packaging even before reading the ingredients list. Metallic dyes are known as 'progressive hair colours' and 'colour restorers'. They are referred to as 'progressive' because hair progressively turns darker and darker upon each subsequent application. The term 'colour restorer' is used because the natural hair colour *appears* to be gradually restored. When the desired colour is reached, the consumer needs to reduce the frequency of application to maintain the colour.

TIP: Remember that while these colours fall within the semi-permanent hair colour section, most do require a skin test before each application.

TIP: Vegetable colours can form an alternative for clients who show an allergy to oxidation colouring.

NOTE: The coating effect of Henna can make the hair resistant to permanent waving.

Metallic hair dyes comprise a minor portion of the home hair-colouring market and currently are very rarely used professionally. Nevertheless, it is crucial for the professional colourist to be informed of the chemical composition, characteristics, and methods of removal, because metals react adversely with oxidation results.

Clients occasionally request chemical services without knowing the incompatibility of metallic colour with professional oxidation products. Consumers generally do not even realise that they used a product containing metal. The colourist must be able to analyse and prescribe safe, professional treatments to avoid hair damage and discolouration.

The metallic coating builds up on the surface of the hair shaft. Repeated treatments leave the hair brittle and conflict with future chemical services that include in their formulation hydrogen peroxide, thioglycolate, ammonia, and/or most other oxidisers.

Resulting damage might be discolouration, breakage, poor permanent waving results, and even destruction to the point of a melted hair shaft due to the heat created in this adverse chemical reaction.

Compound dyes

Compound dyes are a combination of metallic salts or mineral dyes with a vegetable tint. The metallic salts are added to give the product more staying power and to create a wider range of colours. Like metallic dyes, compound dyes are not often used professionally.

Many clients use hair colouring products at home. Therefore, you must be able to recognise and understand their effects. Such colouring agents must be removed and the hair reconditioned prior to any other chemical service.

Hair treated with metallic or any other coating dye looks dry and dull. It is generally harsh and brittle to touch. These colourings usually fade to unnatural tones. Silver dyes have a greenish cast, lead dyes leave a purple colour, and those containing copper turn red.

Test for metallic salts (incompatibility test)

1. In a glass container, mix 30 ml of 20 volume (6%) peroxide and 20 drops of 28% ammonia water.

2. Cut a strand of the client's hair, bind it with tape, and immerse in the solution for 30 minutes.

3. Remove, towel dry, and observe the strand.

Hair dyed with lead will lighten immediately. Hair treated with silver will show no reaction at all. This indicates that other chemicals will not be successful because they will not be able to penetrate the coating.

Hair treated with copper will start to boil and will pull apart easily. This hair would be severely damaged or destroyed if other chemicals such as those found in permanent oxidation colours or perm solutions were applied to it.

Hair treated with a coating dye either will not change or will lighten in spots. This hair will not receive chemical services easily, and the length of time necessary for penetration may very well damage the hair.

Preparations designed to remove metallics and non-peroxide dye solvents may assist in the removal of metallic and coating dyes from the hair. Performing a strand test will indicate whether the metallic deposits have been removed.

Oxidation hair colour

Permanent oxidation hair colours can lighten and deposit colour in one application, a feat performed by no other classification. This ability to create an infinite array of levels, tones, and intensities has made permanent colours irreplaceable in the industry. These tints penetrate the cuticle of the hair and enter the cortical layer (see Figure 6.37). Here, they are oxidised by the peroxide added into colour pigments. These pigments are distributed throughout the hair shaft much like natural pigment (see Figure 6.38).

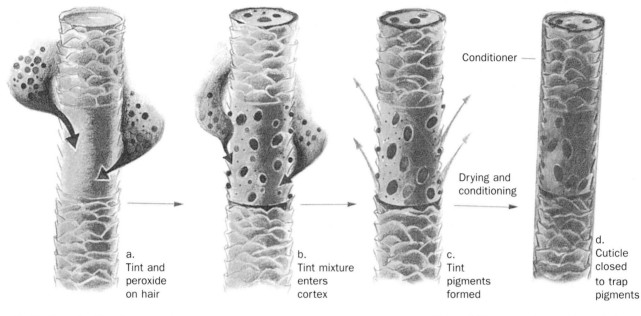

a.
Tint and peroxide on hair

b.
Tint mixture enters cortex

c.
Tint pigments formed

Conditioner —

Drying and conditioning

d.
Cuticle closed to trap pigments

Figure 6.37a Tint and peroxide on hair;
  b Tint mixture enters cortex;
  c Tint pigments formed;
  d Cuticle closed to trap pigments

Application classifications

Permanent hair colour applications are classified as either single-process colouring or double-process colouring.

Single-process colouring achieves the desired colour with one application. Although the application itself may have several different steps, the desired colour is achieved with a single application. Lightening of the hair's natural pigment and deposit of the artificial pigment in the cortex is done simultaneously as the hair colouring product processes. Some examples of single-process colouring are virgin tint applications and tint retouch applications.

Double-process colouring achieves the desired colour upon completion of two separate product applications. It is also known as double-application tinting and two-step colouring. Two examples are bleaching followed by a toner application and pre-softening followed by a tint application. Because the lightening action and the colour deposit are independently controlled, a wider range of hair colour possibilities is opened up for each client.

Hydrogen peroxide

This is available both as a cream and a liquid, and is the most widely-used provider of oxygen for the oxidation process which takes place when oxidation tints and bleaches are applied to hair.

In the case of oxidation tints, the oxygen provided by the hydrogen peroxide causes the development of the colour combining with the dye material within the cortex to form a colour molecule too large to exit the hair shaft.

When bleaching, oxygen also changes the natural pigment of the hair, changing the melanin molecule from a coloured to a colourless compound. Those pigments most easily affected are ash tones and brown shades, then reds and finally yellow.

Figure 6.38 Action of permanent hair colour

3. Part off a section of hair 0.5 cm in depth, using the tail of the application brush.

4. Apply the product to the middle lengths and ends of the hair, to within 1 cm of the scalp (see Figure 6.42). Scalp heat will aid and speed-up colour development at the root area. Application to the middle lengths and ends first will give this area a greater length of time to develop and therefore result in an overall even result.

5. Ensure that all the hair within each mesh of hair is covered by the tint product. Take care not to apply too much product, as this may result in product dripping onto your client, as well as product wastage.

6. From the nape area progress up one side of the back of the head to the crown area. Take care not to press the tinted mesh of hair onto the untinted root areas of other meshes, as this will bring about an uneven result and overprocessing in certain areas.

Figure 6.42 Applying tint to regrowth at crown and top section

Figure 6.43 Applying tint to front regrowth sections

Figure 6.44 Using the accelerator to assist colour development

NOTE: Some manufacturers recommend a one-step application when darkening hair in a first-time application. This means applying the product from the roots to the points in one application. Check the manufacturer's directions.

HEALTH AND SAFETY: Always unplug electrical appliances, using dry hands, once their use is no longer required.

TIP: Avoid sitting your client where draughts of hot or cold air may affect the hair, producing an uneven colour development. A cold room will slow down the development.

7. Once the crown area is reached, start at the nape on the other side of the back and progress up this side of the back to the crown area.

8. Apply the product to the two front sections, taking care not to allow the product to drip onto your client's face or ears.

9. Cross-check your application to ensure that all the hair's middle length is covered by the product.

10. Allow the product to develop, usually for 10 to 15 minutes (check manufacturer's recommendation). Heat may be applied to aid development (subject to manufacturer's directions). This may be applied in the form of a scalp steamer, the method of using which is described on page 37. An accelerator/radiant heater may also be used, methods of use described on page 37. Take care not to allow the product to dry out on the hair.

11. Check the colour development by wiping a strand free of product, using moist cotton wool, and checking the colour against the required outcome, using the shade guide.

12. Once sufficient development has been identified, prepare a fresh supply of the product and apply this to the root area, up to the product already on the middle lengths. This is carried out by taking similar sized sections in the same order as for the first application.

13. Check that all the hair has been coated with the product. Allow to develop, in the same manner as previous. A full processing period will be required for this fresh application of product to the hair.

Figure 6.45 Scalp steamer

Figure 6.46 Applying tint to middle lengths and ends of hair

Figure 6.47 Tint applied to all the hair

14. Check the development of the colour by wiping a strand of hair free of tint using moist cotton wool. Check the resulting colour for evenness and for its match to the desired finished colour.

15. If the development is incomplete, apply product to the test strand and leave to develop further. If the development is complete move your client to the basin area.

Your client should view their new hair colour in natural daylight. They should be made fully aware of how their colour will appear once they leave the salon. The hair will be damaged by the chemicals during the colouring process. Most modern colour products reduce hair damage to a minimum, and contain buffers to reduce this effect and conditioners to compensate. Your client may not be used to handling their hair in its new condition and therefore will require guidance in its after-care. Home care products should be recommended and guidance in their correct use be given to your client, to enable them to maintain their new colour and condition, as well as reduce fade.

Guidance will be required in when to make follow-up visits to the salon.

Figure 6.48 Checking hair colour development

Procedure for retouch application

The fresh growth of hair will require colouring at intervals of approximately one month. This is the job of the professional hair colourist.

Always consult with your client before undertaking a retouch colour. Check if the colour required is the same as the previous colour service given.

1. Put on protective gloves.

2. Begin in the section where the colour change will be the greatest or the hair is most resistant, consult the record card for indication of any particular areas of resistance. If there is no specified area it is usual to start at the back of the head (see Figures 6.39–6.41).

3. Part off a section of hair 0.5 cm in depth, using the tail of the application brush.

4. Apply the product to the regrowth area. If the regrowth is longer than 1.5 cm it should be treated as if it were a first time application. This is because body heat from the scalp does not affect the hair past this point.

5. Ensure that all the regrowth hair within each mesh of hair is covered by the tint product. Take care not to apply too much product, as this may result in product running down the hair, as well as product wastage.

6. From the nape area progress up one side of the back of the head to the crown area. Take care not to press the ends of the hair onto the tinted root areas of other meshes, as this will result in an uneven result and overprocessing in certain areas.

❧ **TIP: Ensure accurate measurement of product to maintain continuity of hair colour.**❧

❧ **TIP: Overlapping colour onto previously coloured hair may result in banding of colour, damage to the hair, and even hair breakage.**❧

143

7. Once the crown area is reached, start at the nape on the other side of the back and progress up this side of the back to the crown area (see Figure 6.42).

8. Apply the product to the two front sections, taking care not to allow the product to drip onto your client's face or ears (see Figure 6.43).

9. Cross-check your application to ensure that all the regrowth is covered by the product.

10. Allow the product to develop, usually for 20 to 35 minutes. Check the manufacturer's recommendation. Heat may be applied to aid development (subject to manufacturer's directions). This may be applied in the form of a scalp steamer: method of use is described on page 37. An accelerator/radiant heater may also be used, its method of use is also described on page 37. Take care not to allow the product to dry out on the hair (see Figure 6.44 and 6.45).

11. Check the colour development by wiping a strand free of product, using moist cotton wool and checking the colour against the required outcome, using the shade guide.

12. Once sufficient development has been identified, consider if the colour of the middle lengths and ends require refreshing. Do not unnecessarily apply colour to the middle lengths and ends as this will result in unnecessary damage to the hair and a progressive darkening (colour build-up). Fresh tint, diluted tint, or semi-permanent colour may be used to refresh the colour in these areas. The choice may depend upon the degree or amount of colour fade (see Figure 6.46).

13. Check that all the hair has been coated with the product. Allow to develop, in the same manner as previously. A full processing period will be required for this fresh application of product to the hair (see Figure 6.47).

14. Check the development of the colour by wiping a strand of hair free of tint using moist cotton wool. Check the resulting colour for evenness and for its match to the desired finished colour (see Figure 6.48).

15. If the development is incomplete, apply product to the test strand and leave to develop further. If the development is complete move your client to the basin area.

Removing the product from the hair

1. Massage the product on the hair and scalp, paying particular attention to the hairline, where this process will help to lift any skin staining (moist tint will remove skin staining at this time). This massage will also help to emulsify the product and aid its easier removal from the hair.

2. Follow the manufacturer's directions in product removal. If you are in doubt about the correct process consult with your line manager, stylist or trainer. In most cases this will include adding a small quantity of warm water to the product on the hair. Massage this to emulsify, add more warm water, massage and then rinse away.

3. Thoroughly rinse the product from the hair.

4. Shampoo the hair thoroughly, using a mild (acid-balanced) shampoo. The acid-balanced shampoo will help to flatten the hair cuticle, prevent any creeping oxidation (continued oxidation action in the hair), and help to return the hair to its normal pH.

5. Apply an anti-oxidation, fixing, finishing rinse to the hair. The exact product to be used will depend on salon procedures and manufacturer's directions.

TIP: Avoid sitting your client where draughts of hot or cold air may affect the hair, producing an uneven colour development. A cold room will slow down the development.

TIP: At this time the scalp may be a little sensitive, so take care to control the water temperature applied to the scalp, and avoid the warmer temperatures.

6. Style the hair.

7. Complete the record card and file or enter onto the computerised data base.

Clean-up

1. Dispose of all disposable supplies and materials.

2. Close containers firmly, wipe them clean and put them in their proper place. Never return unused products to their containers as they may be contaminated and will subsequently contaminate all of the product in the container.

3. Wash and dry all equipment, and place soiled linen in the laundry basket.

4. Clean the working area.

5. Wash and dry your hands.

❶

HIGHLIGHT AND LOWLIGHT EFFECTS IN HAIR COLOURING

Highlighting and lowlighting techniques for hair colouring use lighter or darker shades of hair colour to enhance and accentuate your client's hair colour and hair style (see Figure 6.49). A combination of lighter and darker shades may be used to give depth and dimensions to the hairstyle. A single additional shade may be used to accentuate natural tone in the hair or to define movement in the hairstyle. There are a number of techniques available, some of which produce effects throughout the entire head of hair and others which are designed specifically for small areas of the hairstyle.

Techniques of highlighting and lowlighting

Weaving techniques

There are a number of techniques used to weave small strands of hair from the bulk which may then either be coloured or lightened, or a combination of both. There are a variety of specialist tools to produce this effect, but in most cases the point end of a pin-tail comb is used to weave out the strands of hair. These strands are subsequently separated from the bulk of the hair using aluminium foil, fine film wrap, proprietary brand sachets or tissue.

Client preparation

1. Discuss and negotiate the required result with your client. This will include details of the required overall hairstyle, the required colour effect, the density of the woven sections and the cost of the service. Check any colour record cards available for your client.

2. Carry our predisposition test, 24 – 48 hours beforehand, if a permanent oxidation tint is to be used.

3. Gown your client as for a permanent form of hair colouring.

4. Section the hair, according to the required hairstyle, to give control over the hair when weaving.

Product preparation

1. Prepare the sachets that will be used in the process. When using aluminium foil these are available in prepared batches, already cut to specified lengths. Others come on a continuous roll which must then be cut to slightly more than twice the length of the hair to be coloured. Fold one end of the foil over at approximately 5 mm deep to produce a more rigid band to hold against the root area at the scalp. When using fine film wrap this is cut as it is required, and is used at its full width. Proprietary brands of sachets consist of a plastic-based sachet with a

Figure 6.49 Special effects hair lightening

TIP: A predisposition test is not normally required prior to the application of a bleach product. However if your client has a history of hypersensitivity a skin test may be advisable.

TIP: Remember that once mixed the colouring/bleaching product begins to oxidise and if too long a period elapses before its use it may have fully oxidised before it touches the hair. It will therefore have little or no effect on the hair.

Figure 6.50 Weaving subsection with tail comb.

Figure 6.51 Place hair in foil packets

TIP: To assist in holding aluminium foil in place when laying the hair onto it, apply a small amount of the colouring mix to the foil before locating it in place. Once the hair is laid onto this the adhesion will help to hold the foil and hair together.

TIP: Too much colour product within the sachet may result in seepage onto the rest of the hair.

transparent cover and a mild adhesive strip. If working without assistance a number of these should be opened ready for use. When working on very long hair it may be necessary to join two of these together. Sachets usually come in a variety of lengths. Tissue may be used to separate strands of coloured hair from the rest. The colour product must be of a thick consistency. For this technique, a spatula is required. The strands to be coloured are placed on the spatula and the colour product applied. The spatula is withdrawn and the coloured hair allowed to fall onto the tissue.

2. Prepare a small quantity of the colouring product. As this process can be quite lengthy, small measured quantities of product prepared when required are better than preparing a large quantity at the outset which then deteriorates before it is used on the hair.

3. You will require protective rubber gloves.

Weaving the highlights

1. It is usual to start at the bottom of the hair section, as the woven meshes will hang down and should not be disturbed. Start at that area of the head where the highest degree of colour change is required, or where the hair is most resistant, if the degree of resistance is known.

2. Using the pin tail of the comb, draw off a mesh which is 1 cm deep and then slice off the top 3 mm of this mesh (see Figure 6.50). Allow the larger section to fall and retain the smaller, held firmly outwards from the head, tangle-free.

3. Weave out fine strands to be coloured, by pushing the point of the pin tail (held parallel to the mesh) across the mesh, pressing down at those points when the strand to be coloured is required. When you begin to practise this skill it will be a slow process, however with much practice not only will your speed develop but also your ability to draw off consistent sizes of meshes (see Figure 6.50).

4. Now hold out the woven-off strands from the head while the remainder of the hair is allowed to fall. Place the sachet close to the roots of these strands at the scalp, and then lay the strands onto the foil and apply the colour (see Figure 6.51). Do not apply the colour product all the way to the scalp, as this may result in seepage onto the rest of the hair. Apply to within 5 mm of the scalp: the product will be drawn along the hair to the scalp.

5. Once the colour/bleach mix has been applied to the strands of hair, fold the sachet to secure it on the hair and to retain the product within it. Avoid pressing on the bulk of the sachet as this may cause the product to ooze from the sachet and then contaminate the other hair.

6. Continue to do this throughout the head in a systematic manner. As this can be a lengthy process, check the colour development of those sachets placed earlier as you progress around the head.

7. When making a section at the front hairline, take a parting at a slight angle to the hairline, as this will avoid obvious lines of colour appearing. Avoid locating strands of colour on the parting or on the very edge of the hairline, as the regrowth will be very apparent as the hair grows.

8. Allow the hair to process without additional heat as this can cause the product within the sachet to either become more liquid (if it is an oil-based product) or to expand (all oxidation products do this) and therefore ooze onto adjacent hair and cause unsightly patches of colour.

9. When using permanent hair colours allow the product to process for the full development period following the application of the final sachet.

When using bleach you must check the degree of lift from the earlier made sachets, as these may have fully processed before the later ones. If this is the case remove these sachets and using moist cotton wool remove the bleach from the hair.

10. Once the colour has fully processed take your client to the basin area. Recline them to the basin and then begin rinsing the hair using lukewarm water. As the water floods the hair the sachets may be removed by sliding them from the hair.

11. Rinse the colour from the hair, shampoo using a post-colour shampoo and follow with a pH balance/anti-oxidation conditioner. This will help to prevent creeping oxidation and to close the cuticle flat.

12. Complete your client's record card, noting the products used, the techniques applied and the results.

Clean-up

All used materials should be disposed off. Those highlighting sachets made for repeat use should be washed, dried and stored for future use. Used linen should be disposed of in the laundry bin, and all containers returned to their storage area.

Cap technique

The cap technique involves pulling clean strands of hair through a perforated cap using a hook (see Figure 6.52). This technique is best suited to use on short hair, though there are brands of highlight cap specifically designed for use on long hair. Due to the translucent nature of many brands of highlight cap, it can be difficult to determine the exact position of the highlights in relation to the hairstyle.

Figure 6.52 Draw strands through holes in cap

Preparation of the materials

1. Select the type of cap or material to create the cap, the selection of which will often be personal preference. Proprietary brands of highlight cap can usually be used for several applications. For its first use the holes in the cap will need breaking open, using the hook. Take care not to press the hook hard onto the scalp. The areas for the perforations are usually strengthened to avoid tearing and seepage of the colouring product from the outside surface. The interior of the cap should be lightly coated with talc, as this will enable it to slide into position on dry hair. Polythene sheet or fine film wrap may be used in place of the pre-formed cap. The scalp area is enclosed within the wrap and then secured around the hairline using clear adhesive tape. These styles of caps can be susceptible to tearing for those inexperienced with the technique. Other brands of cap may require the application of heat to tighten them to the head shape.

2. Select the hook size relative to the texture of the hair and the thickness of the strands of hair required. The larger the hook size the greater the size of strand drawn through.

3. Select the colouring products, **do not** mix the product until all of the strands of hair have been drawn through the cap.

Client preparation

This is the same as for woven highlights.

Drawing through the highlights

1. Brush the client's hair into the direction of the hairstyle and then ease the highlight cap into place. You will need to locate the *latex style* by placing your hands on the inside, palms open, and easing the cap into place. Ensure that the cap is tight to the scalp, particularly at the crown area.

❝TIP: Check that your client's ears are not trapped or folded under the latex cap.❞

147

Figure 6.53 Apply lightener to selected strands

TIP: Avoid using colour mixes which are too thin as these may seep through the holes in the cap and therefore result in a blotchy result.

2. Plastic caps are rather like bonnets which are located firmly over the hair and then held in place by a tie under the client's chin. Polythene sheet and fine film wrap is located onto the scalp area as firmly as possible and while it is held in place clear adhesive tape is bound around the hairline. Excess sheet or wrap is then trimmed off, taking care not to cut the hair beneath.

3. Lengths of hair which hang from beneath the cap should be gathered together in the nape and protected from colouring product.

4. Draw the strands of hair through the cap starting at the top of the hairstyle. Gently but firmly push the hook through the cap. As you collect hair in the hook, to ensure that the full length of the hair is coloured, gather hair at the root area. Ease this hair through the cap. The closeness and thickness of the strands depends on the thickness of your client's hair and the required outcome. When a subtle effect is required more fine strands may be drawn through. For a more obvious result fewer thicker strands are drawn through.

5. When all the strands are drawn through, check to ensure that the cap is still firmly against the scalp. Gently grasp the strands between the fingers and pull to ensure that they are fully through the cap, and using the fine teeth of a comb, gently comb the hair to ensure that there are no tangles or partly pulled through strands.

6. Mix the colouring/bleach product and apply this to the hair strands which have been drawn through the cap (see Figure 6.53). Start the application of the product to the top of the head, and section by section paste the product onto the hair in an upward direction. In this manner the product-coated hair will lay on the cap instead of hanging down on your client's face and neck.

7. Process as for other forms of permanent hair colouring. Take care: heat applied may cause oil-based colouring products to become more fluid and these may drip onto the client or seep through the hole in the cap.

8. Check the colour development as for other forms of permanent hair colouring. Once the processing is complete at the basin, rinse the product from the hair and cap. The use of high water pressure may result in wetting your client.

9. Apply a conditioning cream to the strands of hair if no subsequent colouring is required, and ease the cap off the head. The cream acts as a lubricant, preventing drag on the hair which might otherwise cause discomfort and hair damage due to over-stretching.

10. Continue as for the removal of other forms of permanent hair colour.

Clean-up

Dispose of all disposable items in a covered bin. Reusable highlight caps should be rinsed clean, dried and then a fine film of talc applied. Place used linen in the laundry basket and return part-used containers to the storage area.

Outcome	Cause	Action
Scalp irritation	high strength of peroxide: allergy to product	remove product immediately and rinse with cold water: seek medical advice
Hair breakage	over processing overlapping onto previously coloured hair; too early comb through of product; incompatible chemicals	remove immediately; use restructurant; use penetrating conditioner
Uneven result	poor application; uneven application; uneven mixing of product; too large hair sections; seepage of product during highlight process - too much product - incorrect product - incorrect use of applied heat to product - product applied too scalp	spot colour to produce even result
Poor coverage	hair resistant; tint underprocessed; poor quality product; lack of red (white/blond hair);	pre-soften hair; re-colour; spot colour; pre-pigment
Incorrect tone	under processed; base too dark (yellow cast); base to light (green cast); incorrect H_2O_2 use	re-colour/bleach if hair tests confirm tensile strength; pre-pigment and recolour

FURTHER STUDY

I Collect a portfolio of manufacturer's directions that you may use as a reference when using hair colouring products.

I Build a portfolio of your hair colouring achievements which you may use as evidence of your skill as well as forming a tool for communicating your range of skill to your client.

I This chapter introduces you to the basic skills of hair colouring. Find out more about alternative colouring techniques and techniques of corrective colouring.

I Artificial pigment requires specialist techniques to remove it from hair. Consult with your supplier on the products available to do this and then find out how they may be used and what their features and limitations are.

I Recolouring lightened hair can result in the production of unwanted green tones. Pre-pigmentation is the technique use to prevent this. Find out the variety of techniques that may be used for this.

I Many clients seek quick, cost-effective ways of using hair colour to accentuate their hairstyle. Watch the trade press for ideas in these areas.

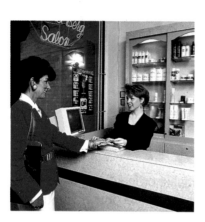

Figure 7.1 The hairdresser as sales person

INTRODUCTION

The customer reception is usually one of the first points of contact that your client has with the salon. This contact may be either by their visit to the salon or by the telephone contact made when your client makes contact to make an appointment. It is therefore at this stage that the initial image of the salon and its customer orientation is perceived by your client.

When your client first visits the salon, their first impression may well be of the facade of the salon and the display provided by the salon window. The new client must make the conscious decision to enter the salon and the way they are greeted and their enquiry handled will shape the view that they have of the salon. The receptionist has a crucial role in this phase of the process, putting the client at ease and ensuring that their needs are identified and fulfilled.

When a new client makes contact by telephone, the response received will be all that influences the client and is therefore a crucial part of the process.

THE ROLE OF THE RECEPTIONIST

The reception function is carried out in a variety of ways from salon to salon. At some the role is carried out by a reception specialist, in others it is carried out by the hair stylists as part of their overall duties. Whoever carries out the function and in whatever way this is done, the objective of the function is the same throughout: to attend to enquiries and to phase appointments effectively to manage the allocation of work and satisfy the client's expectations. This will contribute to the success of the business.

The receptionist's duties

These duties include:

I responding to clients' enquiries, either by telephone or when they visit

I phasing appointments to ensure allocation of work in a way which is achievable by the hairstylist

I informing hairstylists of their client's arrival

I ensuring the comfort of the clients while they wait

I referring clients to the relevant person to fulfil their needs

I calculating client bills and collecting payments

I receiving sales representatives and directing them to appropriate personnel

I providing a point of sale for retail goods (see Figure 7.1).

Qualities of a receptionist

This person should be organised, as they will be organising others and their workloads. They will project the salon's image and will therefore be expected to appear appropriately. Clear speech, together with the ability to communicate effectively, are essential features of a good receptionist.

ATTENDING TO VISITORS TO THE SALON
The clients

All clients who step over the threshold of the salon should be greeted courteously, with a smile and with body language which reflects pleasure in helping them. Greet the client, introducing yourself and asking how you may help them. You will require patience, as clients may be uncertain of their needs. They may require guidance and advice. Establish the client's requirements, which may range from purchasing retail products to seeking advice on their hair care, making an appointment for a hairdressing service to keeping an appointment or even to meeting a business associate in the salon. The receptionist may be able to handle many enquiries, but the client who requires advice and guidance over and above the scope of the receptionist should be invited to wait while a suitable person is informed or a consultation is arranged.

When a client arrives to keep an appointment they should, if possible, be greeted by name, their appointment details checked and the relevant member of staff informed of their arrival.

Advice given to clients, about suitable services or retail products should be accurate and given in a clear manner. If in any doubt the receptionist should seek advice from a specialist within the salon. A knowledge of the features and benefits of services as well as of retail products is an essential aspect of the receptionist's skill. The cost of these should also be readily available.

TIP: When clients visit the salon for the first time, they may feel vulnerable. Ensure that you guide these clients in the procedures of the salon and the location of cloakrooms, toilets and other client facilities. A client who is made aware of what to expect will feel more relaxed and more likely to enjoy their visit.

Things to avoid

Do not:

I keep the client waiting for service while you carry on a conversation about a non-work related issue with a colleague. In all events the client's presence should be acknowledged even if you are unable to attend to them straight away due to a prior commitment

I allow any displeasure or harassment to be reflected in your greeting to the client. The client should be the centre of your attention

I keep a client waiting without informing them of possible delays and reasons for these. In the case of lengthy delays, consider options which the client may prefer, a revised appointment or alternative stylist. Effective phasing of appointments should avoid this occurrence

I eat, drink or smoke at reception. Responding to a client while you are eating or drinking is not a pleasant experience for them. Smoking can be anti-social and odours from this can put your clients off.

Sales representatives

The receptionist will be the first point of contact for the sales representative. Clients to the salon must take precedence over the representative. Check the credentials of the representative: most will carry a business card, which will indicate their name and the company that they represent. Having established their identity, ask them to take a seat in the waiting area and then inform the person with the responsibility for liaising with them. Some salons have a policy that sales representatives may only be seen by appointment with the relevant person and others will meet representatives if they are available. The receptionist must ensure that they are aware of the salon's policy in these matters.

Deliveries of product are usually made to the reception area of the salon. Salons may have policies regarding where goods should be delivered and who is eligible to sign the carrier's dockets, confirming receipt of goods in good order, and the procedure to be adopted.

 Stock control, page 175

Other visitors

Any visitor to the salon should report to the reception. The salon may have policies on how visitors other than clients should be greeted. If in doubt, you should check the visitor's identity and, having seated them in the waiting area, seek advice from the salon management.

These visitors may include local authority representatives, training advisors and awarding body verifiers, business consultants, personal friends and acquaintances. The salon may have policies about members of staff receiving unofficial visits from acquaintances, except in emergencies.

If messages are taken for members of staff or management these should be recorded and passed to the relevant person. When taking messages, the salon may have its own procedures or pro-forma message pads. The detail usually required includes the name of the intended recipient, the name of the message leaver, the date and time of the message, the actual detail of the message and any action or response that is required. The salon may have a procedure for passing messages to ensure that they are passed promptly and that follow-up action is taken.

USE OF THE TELEPHONE

The telephone forms a link between the salon and its clientele, enabling them to make contact without the need to actually visit the salon. With this in mind it is important that this service is available for as much time throughout the working day as possible. Personal telephone conversations should be avoided, and in many cases are prohibited, except in emergency. Conversations with clients should be clear and effective but at the same time as brief as possible without making the client feel rushed. When the telephone is in use other clients cannot make contact with you.

The telephone may also be used in a proactive manner in order to generate business, a method of checking on clients who have perhaps not visited the salon for some time and a way of reminding them of the services that you offer.

In cases of emergency, perhaps due to a member of staff's unplanned absence due to ill health, the telephone provides a method of contacting clients and rescheduling them.

Responding to the call

The telephone should be answered promptly. Your salon may have a policy in always responding to the telephone within three rings. This should be considered good practice (see Figure 7.2). The caller should be informed of the name of the salon, who is responding to the call, and an invitation or offer of service, for example: 'This is Salon Hair, Paula speaking, how may I help you?'

Speak clearly to the caller who is making an appointment, repeat the detail of the date, time, the service to be offered and if relevant the stylist who will be undertaking the task. If in doubt about the spelling of a client's name ask the client to spell this out for you. This is not usually considered impolite. When you book clients who are visiting the salon for the first time, check that they have an idea of the average cost of treatments. Your salon may have specific requirements when making appointments, particularly if a computerised appointment system is used, as details of the client will be 'called up' for checking when the appointment is entered. Remember to thank the caller for calling at the end of the conversation.

When responding to a telephone call where a message is taken, read this back to the caller to check the accuracy of the message taken.

When speaking to a telephone caller, remember that background noise from the reception area may be heard. Confidential conversations may be overheard, if you must keep the client waiting while you source information use the mute button on the telephone, if available, so that comments not intended to be heard by the client do not become communicated.

Figure 7.2 The telephone is an important part of the salon business

Should a client telephone while the receptionist is busy dealing with another client, the telephone should be answered and the caller asked if they can 'hold' while the current client's transaction is dealt with. If the client states that they cannot hold, then a return telephone number may be requested with an undertaking for the receptionist to return the call at the earliest instant. It is important that this undertaking is subsequently not neglected.

THE APPOINTMENT SYSTEM

Every salon requires a record of planned appointments for its clients. The record not only serves to ensure that the hairdresser has a planned rota of clients with which to work and will assist the stylist in planning their working day, it will also serve as a reconciliation document, a check of takings by the stylist against the anticipated income from a number of clients.

The manual appointment book

The appointment schedule usually takes the form of a written appointment book, with a page per day, containing columns allocated to particular hairstylists and specialists which is divided into time slots, usually in fifteen-minute intervals. The client's name, contact telephone number and the nature of the service required are then entered in the relevant stylist's column at the appropriate time of the day.

The receptionist must be aware of the stylist's competencies and the time that they require to complete services. This will enable them to realistically phase clients to ensure maximum efficiency without delay to the client.

The computerised reception system

More and more hairdressing salons are using computerised systems to retain their customer information and to phase their appointments. In most systems the computer software will have built in to them the range of services available from the salon and the timings which are required for each stylist to undertake these tasks. This is usually linked to an automatic billing system that not only calculates the client's bill but is also often capable of re-booking appointments and generating reminders of these appointments for clients.

General guidance

The same guidance would be given as for when confirming appointments with clients via the telephone. Ensure that you communicate effectively, ensuring that the client is aware of the time and date of the next appointment, together with details of the service to be provided and the stylist who will provide this. Always confirm the appointment by completing an appointment card. This card will remind the client of the date and time of their next appointment as well as being a reminder to your client of the business, enabling them to recommend and direct new clients to you easily.

Should someone request an appointment with a particular hairstylist for a particular day and time when that stylist is not available, there are several ways to handle the situation:

I If the client regularly uses that one hairstylist, suggest other times when the stylist is available.

I If the client cannot come in at any of those times, suggest another stylist.

I If the client is unwilling to try another hairstylist, offer to call the client if there is a cancellation at or near the desired time.

TIP: If you are dealing with a telephone request for an appointment which cannot be met, do not say 'no'. Always offer alternatives. 'No' can terminate the conversation leaving no area for negotiation.

155

When clients pay their bill at the end of the service, always offer to make further appointments for them. This will help to ensure repeat visits by clients and maintains the relationship between the salon and client.

RECEIVING CUSTOMER PAYMENTS

Part of the role of the receptionist is that of handling client payments. This requires the skills of numeracy and tact.

Following the treatment the client's total bill must be calculated. Salons may have differing ways of doing this. In some cases the hairstylist informs the receptionist of the various services and items that are to be added to the bill. In other salons each individual who contributes to the client's treatments reports this to the receptionist who then maintains a record of the service given and subsequently calculates the bill based upon this information.

Provided that all details of all services are correctly 'keyed' in, a computerised client reservation and recording system will then calculate the client's bill and will record all treatments. Many electronic tills will calculate the amount of change to be given to the client, if required. Some may also record the stylist's name so that commissions and performance figures can be established. Each day a cash 'float' is required so that change may be given to clients. This consists of an agreed amount of cash in small denominations. The receptionist should check the level of the float and record it, so that it may be accurately deducted when the takings are reconciled (actual takings are compared to recorded takings). The receptionist should operate the cash flow to avoid running out of a range of cash for change. A reserve may be kept in a safe and the receptionist should be aware of how to easily obtain this and should forecast when it may be required so as to save shortages at crucial times.

Unless otherwise stated on the price list, prices charged are assumed to include Value Added Tax (VAT) at the current appropriate rate.

The salon receptionists must make themselves aware of acceptable forms of payment within the salon. These may include:

I cash

I cheques

I credit cards

I cash equivalents

I vouchers.

Cash payments

The most often used form of payment for services, coinage of the realm, is accepted in all salons. When receiving cash as payment note the following:

I Always count and agree the actual payment before the cash is placed in the cash drawer.

I When change is required, retain the original payment outside the cash drawer while change is calculated. This can help to avoid disagreements about the amount of the initial payment.

I Always follow the salon's policy in checking the validity of bank notes used for payments.

I It is not usual to open a cash drawer just to obtain change for a client; the opening of the till should normally coincide with a transaction.

Payment by cheque

Most salons accept payment from clients by cheque. Some do, however, set a minimum level above which the cheque payment should be, usually to offset the bank charges levied against the business for paying in the cheque. When receiving a cheque, note the following procedures:

I The cheque should be signed in the presence of the receiver. The remainder of the detail may have been printed for the client by a computerised till or may have been written by the client.

I Check that the days date is correct, with the correct year, that it is made payable to the correct company name and that the amount payable is correct both in writing and in figures.

I Most businesses require that a cheque payment be supported by a cheque guarantee card. If this is the case, the client should be asked to write the card number on the reverse side of the cheque. The receptionist should check the accuracy of the number, that the card will guarantee the cheque to the required level – this amount (usually £50 or £100) is indicated on the card – that the signature on the cheque is the same as that on the card, and that it is tendered within the card's start and expiry dates.

I If there is doubt about the validity of the card it should be retained by the receptionist while checks are made. If in any doubt about the salon procedures for doing this consult with your line manager.

It is not normal practice to cash cheques for clients without the agreement of the salon management, or to give cash change for cheques made out to greater amounts than that of the bill. It is unwise to accept cheques that are not made payable to a specific name, or where any detail is incomplete.

> **TIP: Remember, the checking of the validity of a cheque guarantee card or credit card can cause some clients embarrassment, therefore this process should be carried out with discretion and the utmost courtesy to the client.**

Credit card payments

Payment by this method is accepted by many but not all businesses. Agreement between the business and the particular credit card company is required. The business pays a percentage of each card transaction to the card company. Always follow your salon's policy in receiving these cards. These transaction may be completed either via an electronic point of sale, which links direct with the card company and validates and records the transaction direct. The use of sales vouchers either printed via a computerised till or by hand may also be used. Some general notes of guidance are:

I Always check that the card is valid and within the start and expiry dates.

I If completing a sale voucher by hand, use a ballpoint pen, ensuring that the writing can be seen on all copies. The details from the card may be transferred to the sales voucher using an imprinter. Pass the top copy of the voucher to the client, for their record. All others to be placed in the cash drawer.

I Check that the card is not the subject of a warning notice. From time to time card companies will circulate a listing of card numbers which should not be accepted, and if used should be retained by the salon who should inform the card company.

I Do not accept damaged or torn cards, particularly if the signature strip has been partially or completely removed.

I Each business will have been set a 'floor limit', the level of payment above which authorisation must be obtained from the card company if the payment is to be guaranteed. This may be done by a simple telephone call and a 'transaction number' recorded on the sales voucher; you will need to have at hand your 'merchant number' when making this call.

Figure 8.1 Be caring and objective

INTRODUCTION

As a professional hairdresser you will project an image which is manifold, both as a professional hair artist and as a socially conscious person, aware of current fashion trends who may be both caring and objective when advising clients (see Figure 8.1). Your development in the profession of hairdressing is integral with all of the other tasks that you carry out. It is impossible to separate your development from the day to day work that you perform. As a novice hairdresser you will always be learning, either from formal training sessions or by watching and being involved with the effective running of the business. Every experience that you have in this profession must be viewed as a learning process which enables you to develop your skills further.

Always reflect upon your performance of a task. Consider what you did well and build on this; for those areas where you feel that you did not perform so well, be objective and consider what changes you should make in your future actions which will improve yourself. Be aware of who you may approach for advice and guidance in these matters and at what time this may be most appropriate.

As a hairstylist the learning and development process never ends. In the early stages it may be that you have basic skills to acquire and you must develop a work ethos that ensures that you approach your work with enthusiasm, remembering that in a service industry your performance with your client is what ensures their return and therefore your ongoing success. Not only will you be developing your practical skills but also your social skills. Very rarely will you work in isolation. At all levels you will need to be able to interact with colleagues, supporting each other in your workplace, and this will be seen by your clientele. You must therefore develop skills of working together as part of a team, as well as relating with your client on a 'one to one' basis.

Fashion does not stand still, so neither will the requirements of your clients or your employer. As a commercial hair stylist you must keep abreast of both current and emerging fashion trends. This may be achieved in a variety of ways which are mentioned elsewhere in this book. Your role within the hairdressing salon will also develop. You will be expected, at certain stages, to take on responsibilities. These may appear quite minor – preparing work stations, for example – or they may take the form of supervisory skills, allocation and checking of work being carried out by others, or even making judgements on other people's performance. All are important and may be essential to the running of the business. They all require different skills, which must be developed and do not normally happen without some kind of planning.

As an employee in a business, you will interact with your line manager. You must take on the skills of negotiation and interaction not only with your colleagues, but with those for whom you have responsibility, and with your line managers.

PROFESSIONAL IMAGE

Image is the pivotal focus for hairdressing. Each hair stylist and salon will seek to project an image which will relate to a particular type of clientele. This will usually be shown by the appearance and manner of the hair stylist together with the style of hairdressing produced. Some salons will have an image which will focus on a specific segment of the market and will be quite clearly defined, whether by the salon decor, the salon facade, the atmosphere generated or a combination of all three. Other salons will have a professional image which will be attractive to a wider market segment in terms of gender, age and socio-economic grouping.

PHYSICAL DEVELOPMENT

As a hairdresser, the main tool that you use is your body. Take care of this machine to ensure that it serves you throughout your career. Your service to your client is achieved partly through the skills that you have developed, and partly through the atmosphere of relaxation and pleasure that you create. You must be physically able to provide this service throughout the working week, and this means taking care of your health.

Personal health and hygiene

For your client to feel at ease and relaxed while in your company, you must be pleasant to be with, and this means attending to your personal hygiene. Open sores or cuts on exposed areas of the skin should be covered with a waterproof dressing, helping to prevent the spread of any infection. This is often a requirement of the local bye-laws affecting the registration of hairdressing salons with local authorities.

As a hairdresser, you will work in very close proximity to your client, so you must be aware of their discomfort if you have body odour or bad breath. Smoking will leave an odour on your breath and clothes which can be most unpleasant, particularly for non-smoking clients. Your client may also find odours from strongly flavoured foods unpleasant, and these may linger for some considerable time. Put yourself in your client's position and consider how you would react to these situations. Remember that your client has a choice of which salon they visit.

As a member of a team, remember that these same factors may affect your working relationships with your colleagues.

You must consider your salon's policy with regard to working with clients when your are suffering with colds or disorders which may be contagious, and you should make yourself aware of legislative regulations that may have an effect.

Care of your feet

As a hairdresser you will spend a great deal of time on your feet. Proper foot care will help you maintain a good posture and a cheerful attitude. Sore feet or poorly-fitting shoes can cause great discomfort (see Figure 8.2).

Shoes

Try to wear shoes with low, broad heels and cushioned insoles. They give you support and balance, and help to maintain good posture, offsetting the fatigue that can result from hours of standing. It also helps if you can stand on a carpeted or cushioned surface.

Daily foot care

After bathing, apply cream or oil and massage each foot for 5 minutes. Remove the cream or oil and apply an antiseptic foot lotion. Regular pedicures that include cleansing, removal of callused skin, massage, and toenail trims will keep your feet at their best. When your feet ache, chiropodists recommend that you soak your feet alternately in warm and cool water. See a chiropodist if you suffer from corns, bunions, ingrown toenails, or other foot disorders.

Healthy lifestyle

You should practise stress management through relaxation, rest, and exercise. Avoid substances that can negatively affect your good health, such as cigarettes, alcohol, and drugs.

 TIP: Potential clients will often form opinions about you as a hair stylist by your appearance.

 TIP: You may be able to insure against loss of use of certain parts of your body, your hands for example, which may prevent you from carrying out your hairdressing role.

For more information about this see Chapter 10, pages 179–185

Figure 8.2 For comfort and to maintain good posture, wear well-fitted, low-heeled shoes

PHYSICAL PRESENTATION

Your posture, walk, and movements all make up your physical presentation. People form opinions about you by the way you present yourself. Do you stand straight or slouch; do you walk confidently or do you drag your feet? Your physical presentation is part of your professional image and can help to reduce fatigue.

Good posture

Good posture not only improves your personal appearance by presenting your stature to advantage and creating an image of confidence, it also prevents fatigue and many other physical problems (see Figures 8.3 and 8.4). As a hairdresser you spend most of your working time on your feet, so you should develop good posture as early as possible through regular exercise and self-discipline.

Figure 8.3 Good posture   Figure 8.4 Five defective body postures

Physical presentation on the job

To prevent muscle aches, back strain, discomfort, fatigue, and other problems, and to maintain an attractive image, it is very important to practise good physical presentation while performing work activities (see Figures 8.5 to 8.6).

Checkpoints of good posture

I Crown of head reaching upward while chin is kept level with the floor.

I Neck is elongated and balanced directly above the shoulders.

I Chest up; body is lifted from the breastbone.

I Shoulders are level, held back and down, yet relaxed.

I Spine is straight, not curved laterally or swayed from front to back.

I Abdomen is flat.

I Hips are level (horizontally) and protrude neither forward nor back.

I Knees are slightly flexed and positioned directly over the feet with the ankles firm.

Figure 8.5 To avoid back strain, maintain good posture when giving a shampoo

Figure 8.6 Poor posture

Basic stance for women

- Place most of your weight on your right foot and point your toes straight ahead in a straight line.
- Place your left heel close to the heel or instep of your right foot and point the toes slightly outward.
- Bend your left knee slightly inward (see Figure 8.7).

Basic stance for men

- Place your feet apart, but not wider than your shoulder width.
- Distribute your weight evenly over both feet.
- Your knees should be neither rigid nor bent.
- Your toes should point straight ahead or one or both feet should point slightly outward.
- For a more relaxed stance, bend one knee slightly while shifting some of your weight to the opposite foot (see Figure 8.8).

Good manners should not be viewed as a sign of weakness. As members of a team respect for each other is best gained by your actions towards each other. A well-mannered approach to a colleague is more likely to generate a similar response, whereas an ill-mannered approach is more likely to be met with a mirrored response which may then escalate or at least create resentment.

Mannerisms

Gum chewing and nervous habits such as tapping your foot or playing with your hair and personal items detract from your personal effectiveness. Yawning, coughing, and sneezing should be concealed when in the presence of others. Control body language that reveals negative communication, for example, sarcastic or disapproving facial grimaces. Pleasant facial expressions and attractive gestures and actions should be your goal.

 Client care procedures, page 13

HUMAN RELATIONSHIPS AND YOUR PROFESSIONAL ATTITUDE

Human relationships involve the psychology of getting along well with others. Your professional attitude is expressed by your own self-esteem, your confidence in your abilities, and by the respect you show others.

Good habits and practices acquired during your training lay the foundation for a successful career in hairdressing.

Working with clients

The following are guidelines for good human relations that will help you to gain confidence and deal successfully with your clients.

I Always greet a client by name, with a pleasant tone of voice. Address a client by his or her last name (Mrs Smith, Mr Jones, Miss Allen) unless the client prefers first names and if it is customary to use first names in your salon (if you are in doubt check with your line manager). When greeting a new client introduce yourself to your client and establish their name as rapidly as possible either by consulting the appointment book or by asking your client direct.

I Plan your client's appointments to allow yourself adequate time to carry out the tasks with, if possible, time to react to any additional requests your client has. You should make an overall view of your appointments to try, if possible, to spread your workload evenly over your normal working times. This can help to reduce peaks of extreme pressure or quiet periods which provide a better pace of work and allow you to react to changing circumstances, such as the additional workload created by absence from work of colleagues.

Customer reception, pages 151–159

I Phasing client appointments to enable work to be carried out on more than one client at any one time, when relevant, will improve your efficiency. This may be during the shampooing period, if this is carried out by an assistant, following consultation, while the processing of chemical treatments is taking place or while other specialists within the salon are working on your client.

I Be alert to your client's mood. Some clients prefer quiet and relaxation, others like to talk. Be a good listener and confine your conversation to the client's needs. Never gossip or tell stories.

I Topics of conversation should be carefully chosen. Friendly relations are achieved through pleasant conversations. Let your client be the guide in the topic of conversation. In a business setting it is best to avoid discussing controversial topics such as religion and politics, topics that relate to your personal life such as personal problems, or subjects relating to other people, such as another client's behaviour, poor workmanship of fellow workers or competitors, or information given to you in confidence.

I Confidential details about your clients, addresses, telephone numbers, holiday arrangements, should not be disclosed to others, unless authorised by the client or a responsible person in the business.

I Make a good impression by looking the part of the successful hairstylist, and by speaking and acting in a professional manner at all times.

I Cultivate self-confidence, and project a pleasing personality.

I Show interest in the client's personal preferences. Give your undivided attention. Maintain eye contact and concentrate totally on your client.

I Use tact and diplomacy when dealing with problems you may encounter.

I Be capable and efficient in your work.

I Be punctual. Arrive at work on time (give yourself sufficient time to prepare yourself for work) and keep appointments on schedule. Plan each day's schedule so that you manage your time effectively.

I Develop your business and sales abilities. Use tact when suggesting additional services or products to clients. Be aware of the features and benefits of products retailed within your salon. You should know salon prices so that you may easily inform your clients of their commitment.

I Avoid saying anything which may sound as if you are criticising, condemning, or putting down a client's opinions.

I Keep informed of new products and services so you can answer clients' questions intelligently.

I Continue to add to your knowledge and skills.

I Be ethical in all your dealings with clients and others with whom you come in contact.

I Always let the client see that you practise the highest standards of hygiene.

I Avoid criticising your competitors.

Be aware of your level of responsibility when dealing with clients. As a member of a team which provides services to members of the public, you may be able to make decisions on some issues but not on others. If you are in doubt check this with your line manager.

Do not allow concerns or problems raised by clients to be ignored: they should be dealt with immediately. If these must be referred to another member of staff, this should be done promptly and discreetly. Do not discuss clients or their concerns with colleagues or in front of clients.

Working as part of a team

The following are guidelines for good human relations that will help you to gain confidence and perform successfully with your colleagues.

I As a member of a team, you should make yourself aware of the structure of the team, who your line manager is, who is the overall team leader/manager and what are the responsibilities of the individual team members. There will be those who are responsible for particular tasks or functions within the salon.

I Find out precisely what is expected of you as a member of the team. What are your duties? Who are you responsible to? Who do you approach for advice and guidance? Be prepared to respond to requests for guidance, if this responsibility is within your capability and responsibility.

TIP: Remember, while discussing issues with your client others, with differing views, may be listening.

169

TIP: If you are to carry out your role within the salon, you must ensure that you are aware of what is expected of you in your job.

I As a team member, you will interact with others. As a junior member of a team your role will be more responsive rather than initiative, but you will have a role with defined parameters of personal responsibility. As a more established member of a team your role will evolve often into a more responsible function and gradually may take on supervisory functions, at various levels.

I In the supervisory function, the needs of others should be anticipated and if possible advice and guidance given, or, if necessary, arrangements made for others to do this.

I Requests for assistance by colleagues should be viewed positively. Take care to ensure that your own duties are not neglected in your attempts to assist others. If you are in doubt consult with your line manager about which tasks should be given priority. In an emergency, all possible help should be given, particularly when people may be at risk. Do not undertake tasks for which you are not trained, or use equipment with which you are unfamiliar.

I When you are not actively busy, as a member of a team you should be prepared to offer help and assistance in tasks that you can do to other members of the team.

I Deal with all disputes and differences in private. Take care of all problems promptly. If problems cannot be resolved your line manager should be informed.

Remember that the team is only as strong as its weakest member. Every member of a team is important to ensure success. Responsibilities, no matter how unimportant they may appear, should be taken seriously. As a team member ensure that you are fully aware of what is expected of you by the rest of the team. Should you be unable to undertake certain tasks, you should discuss this with your functional manager, to gain suitable training/instruction.

Team meetings are ideal occasions to raise issues that are relevant to the team. Be prepared to listen to others as well as putting your own thoughts forward. As a team member you must be prepared to accept justified constructive feedback, as well as being able to give this. When giving comment it can help to consider how you might best prefer to receive such comment and use this as guidance in how to undertake this.

TIP: Your line manager is that person to whom you are responsible in decision making, your functional manager is that person to whom you are responsible when carrying out specific tasks.

Personal career development

The following are guidelines for good human relations that will help you to gain confidence and perform successfully within your career in hairdressing.

For successful career progression you should have a planned route (*a career action plan*). Consider what you wish to achieve within your career, and when determining this consider your strengths and weaknesses. Chart how you might achieve these goals. Consider what experiences and training you need to achieve these expectations, being realistic in considering a time scale. As you progress within your career, review your career action plan. Be prepared to amend the plan in the light of your experience. It may turn out that you achieve milestones within your plan sooner than expected. This will necessitate a change in part of the plan. The reverse may also apply. In the experience of work you may decide that your original goals no longer apply and you wish to amend these. The career action plan is a dynamic document, always prepared to respond to change. In the light of changed expectations the route to achieve this will need to be mapped out. The entire process may be done either formally as part of a work review and appraisal process or very informally as a personal thought process. Without a career action plan, achievement will occur more by accident than by design, and time and experience may be wasted.

As part of your career development consider the following:

I Objectively review your performance.

I Identify your strengths and weaknesses; awareness of these can help you to capitalise on the former and address the latter.

I Make the most of opportunities to learn and develop skills;

I Always be prepared to watch specialists work (subject to available time).

I Participate in any available training activities.

I Be prepared to seek advice on issues relating to your job or your learning.

I Be prepared to participate fully in salon activities which will give experience through which learning will take place.

As part of your employment you may be involved in the process of appraisal and review. This is an opportunity, with your line manager or personnel officer or training manager, to review your performance since the previous appraisal, and plan future work. This process may focus on evaluating your performance to date and/or your career action plan and/or planning/responding to your training and development requirements. This becomes your opportunity to review your performance and to highlight those achievements that you consider noteworthy; advice may be given on areas of possible improvement (this should centre around your job description), and to negotiate and agree further training.

The hairdressing industry involves constant evolution of fashion, techniques and new equipment. The experienced hairdresser must learn continuously if they are to maintain the currency of their skills.

FURTHER STUDY

I Awareness of body language can be an important tool in developing/controlling the client/hairdresser relationship. This area should be developed by the hairdresser.

I Maintain an awareness of emerging fashion trends and their associated techniques.

I Create your own career action plan and review this regularly.

I Draw up a list of what you consider to be your strengths (things you do well or are good at) and your weaknesses (things you do less well or are not so good at). Use this list to help to identify areas that you should develop.

I Find out what equipment is required for each process carried out in your salon which you are involved in.

Review questions

1. What is a career action plan?
2. How should exposed cuts be treated, while working with clients?
3. What style of heels are best suited to be worn by the hairdresser, while at work?
4. To reduce fatigue, how should the hairdresser's spine be positioned while working on the client?
5. What advantage is there in phasing customer appointments?

6. Suggest two topics of conversation that should be avoided, with your client.

7. Of what detail about retail products should the hairdresser be aware?

8. At what stage, during the hairdressing process, should clients' concerns be dealt with?

9. What is the ideal occasion to raise issues that are relevant to a working team?

10. Suggest one focus that an appraisal interview may follow.

9 Effective use of resources

The information in this chapter affects all other areas in the book. It provides the essential knowledge to help you understand the concepts and practices of resource control in the hairdressing business.

CONTENTS

Health, safety and security in the salon,
pages 179–183

HEALTH AND SAFETY: Products which release gases (such as hydrogen peroxide) are best stored in opaque plastic containers. If glass containers are used, a space for expansion must be left inside the container. The gases released cause increases in pressure which can cause the bottle to explode when handled. Light and heat can accelerate the release of gas.

As new stock arrives, the old stock should be drawn forward and the newer replenishments put behind this. Partially used containers, tubes of tint etc. should be used before new products are opened, provided that the product already opened is still in good condition. It may be necessary to obtain permission from the manager to dispose of part-used containers if they are no longer usable.

Quantities of stock should be stored in a secure area. This area should be dark, dry and cool with a minimum of temperature variance. This will avoid excessive deterioration of stock. Shelves containing stock should be secure. It is not advisable to store substances which are corrosive above eye level, in case they spill onto the user. Glass bottles should not be stored above head height, to reduce the risk from breakage if dropped.

Inflammable substances may need to be secured in a flame-resistant cabinet.

Products which may react with each other should not be stored together. The salon owner/stock controller will have made assessments of any risks involved in the storage, movement and use of products. If you are in any doubt about how to handle stock seek advice from your manager or trainer.

Take care when moving stock and equipment. Lift heavy products with your back straight (see Figure 9.3) bending at the knees. Do not attempt to lift more than you can reasonably cope with; if in doubt seek assistance. If stock must be obtained from shelves above eye level, stand only on appropriate steps, do not overextend yourself, risking strain or a fall (see Figure 9.4)

Figure 9.3 Always lift heavy items in the correct manner

Figure 9.4 Do not over-extend yourself when handling stock above head height

EFFICIENT USE OF RESOURCES

Wasteful use of any resource will have a detrimental effect upon the business. If you are in doubt about salon procedures and requirements regarding use of resources, consult your line manager or trainer. Here are some basic guidelines which should be adopted by all:

I Turn off electric lights when they are not required, provided that they do not produce a hazardous environment.

I When shampooing turn off the water supply while massaging.

I Apply only sufficient shampoo to cleanse: applying too much shampoo will result in additional time and water being wasted removing the excess lather.

I Do not leave electrical appliances operating when no longer required.

TIP: Manufacturers provide guidance on the rate of use of bulk-supplied products and the number of applications which may be obtained. If you are unsure of the correct amount of a product to use, seek advice from your manager or trainer.

| Rotate stock and use up previously started stock, provided it is still in good condition and not contaminated.

| Plan your appointments to make the most effective use of your time.

| The telephone is a link for the salon to its clientele; do not use it for personal calls, or extend telephone conversations which may prevent a potential client making contact.

| Following manufacturer's guidelines in correct methods of using equipment will reduce unintentional damage.

| To avoid wastage use measured quantities of products.

There are risks involved when intentionally using products and equipment for purposes other than for those for which they were intended. This may neutralise any responsibility that a manufacturer has for the products that it produces. It may also impact upon any compensation available, via insurance, should damage result from this. If you have been instructed in the correct usage and then misuse the product and equipment you may put yourself and/or your colleagues at risk and may also reduce any compensation which you may obtain should an industrial accident result.

Should you identify potential alternative or additional use of resources or identify improvements these should be communicated to your manager or trainer and their agreement and support gained before you implement them. These suggestions may form part of a development exercise for the salon's staff team at a later date.

FURTHER STUDY

| Review your own use of resources and try to act on any areas of potential improvement identified.

| Ensure that you are fully aware of your responsibility, within the hair-dressing salon, with regard to the correct storage and display of products.

Review questions

1. Suggest two resource items that will require monitoring before each working day.

2. What is stock rotation?

3. How should you protect yourself when topping up potentially hazardous materials?

4. How should spillages of liquids be dealt with?

5. What are the ideal conditions for the storage of stock?

6. How should heavy products be lifted?

INTRODUCTION

The maintenance of health and safety at work is the responsibility of everyone. Each person working in the hairdressing salon has a legal requirement to take reasonable care of themselves and not intentionally to put themselves or others at risk by their actions or omissions. Employers have considerable responsibilities within this area, but all employees have a duty to comply with reasonable requests that employers may make of them in their efforts to make the workplace safe.

GENERAL SALON HYGIENE

A hairdressing salon, due to the warm, moist atmosphere and the numbers of people who pass through the doors each day, is an ideal place for the spread of infection and contagious disorders. Section 77 of the Public Health Act, 1961, empowers local authorities to make bye-laws for the registration of premises and health hygiene within them. These bye-laws may differ slightly between authorities, but they are all legally enforceable.

Hygiene within the salon is not only a legal requirement, it must also be highly desirable from everybody's point of view. Your clients visiting the salon will wish to feel safe from the risk of infection. As someone employed in the salon, and therefore spending much of your time in this environment, you too will wish to feel safe, and the salon owner will view this as an essential aspect for successful business.

It is not always satisfactory just to be hygienic: your clients must see that this is the case. This will be reflected by the hygienic behaviour of all staff in the salon, and the high profile given to hygiene. There are three aspects to hygiene in the salon:

I cleanliness and hygiene of the premises and its provisions for hygiene

I cleanliness and hygiene of the tools and equipment

I cleanliness and hygiene of those employed within the salon.

Cleanliness and hygiene of the premises and their provisions for hygiene

All surfaces should be easily cleaned. This includes work surfaces, basins, walls and floors. Hair clippings can be difficult to remove from some surfaces. Floors should be swept daily and cleaned at least once a week. There should be covered bins for hair clippings and other waste materials, and these should be emptied, once full, and at least once a day.

Remember, when cleaning work surfaces using cleaning products, always follow the manufacturer's directions, including the use of protective clothing if required. Products used for cleaning and sterilising surfaces are sometimes flammable.

Cleanliness and hygiene of tools and equipment

Gowns and towels used on your clients, should be freshly washed before use. Tools should be washed and sterilised between use on your clients. In the salon you will find various methods used to sterilise tools. These include; autoclaves, ultra-violet light cabinets and sterilising fluids.

The autoclave

This is a steamer which produces steam at high pressure, allowing high temperatures to be achieved. Due to the high temperatures used, the autoclave is only suitable for use on tools which are not damaged by heat. It is therefore not suitable for use on vulcanite or plastic combs, scissors with plastic inserts or for hair brushes.

TIP: If your job is to clean surfaces and empty bins, look on this as part of the team's work to maintain the correct environment for your clients. Remember, your clients will not be impressed by floors which are littered with hairs or bins which are full to overflowing.

Take care when using an autoclave. Always follow the manufacturer's directions for safe use. The outer casing will usually become hot, and you should always allow adequate time for the pressure within to drop and to cool before opening to remove tools.

Ultra-violet cabinet

This cabinet uses ultra-violet light to sterilise those surfaces that the light rays touch. As a result it is only effective for tools which can be totally exposed to the light on all surfaces, so it may be necessary to turn tools to ensure coverage. To sterilise effectively, tools must be clean and dry when placed in these cabinets. You should not expose yourself to this light.

Sterilising fluids

These are possibly the most widely used means for sterilising tools in the hairdressing salon. Tools should be cleaned before being immersed in the fluids. Fluids should be changed regularly as they:

I rapidly lose their strength. Some have colour detectors to indicate their strength.

I lose their efficiency when the fluid becomes dirty.

Some fluids attack the surface of metallic tools and may make cutting tools blunt. Aerosol sterilising fluids are available which are particularly useful for use on cutting tools.

Before sterilising tools, always wash and dry them, as the presence of dirt, dust and moisture may impede the effects of the sterilising fluid.

Cleanliness and hygiene of those employed in the salon

It is anticipated that hairdressers will be dressed appropriately, wearing protective overalls or uniforms that are worn exclusively at work. Overalls or protective clothing should be washable and kept hygienic for use at work.

The Personal Protective Equipment at Work Regulations 1992 require that suitable protective equipment is provided for employees who may be exposed to risk while at work. This usually means the provision of protective gloves for your use when handling perm lotion, hydrogen peroxide, tints and any other product where the manufacturer's directions indicate this. Protective goggles may also be required in certain circumstances. **As an employee, you should report to your employer any loss or damage to personal protective equipment.**

SAFETY IN THE SALON

Safety legislation requires that all employers should provide a safe working environment and as an employee you have a responsibility to work within the guidelines of safety for the salon. If your salon staff team has five or more people in it, there will be a written health and safety policy. This will give you guidance about:

I who is responsible within the salon for aspects of health and safety

I reporting accidents

I first aid procedures

I emergency procedures.

You may receive training about health and safety and in the particular provisions and procedures for your salon. Some features of safe working may be common sense but may not be apparent to all. In the sketch (see Figure 10.1) there are a number of unsafe practices: can you find them?

TIP: Follow manufacturer's directions in the correct and safe use of sterilising equipment and products.

HEALTH AND SAFETY: Some fluids may be poisonous; alcohol based fluids may be flammable or produce flammable vapour.

Working with others, pages 161–172

Hair which is in its unstretched state consists of 'alpha' keratin; when stretched it becomes 'beta' keratin, remaining in this state until it absorbs moisture and returns to its natural shape and its 'alpha' keratin form.

Preparing your client

Following consultation gown your client to protect their clothes, and shampoo if appropriate.

Setting aids

The set will last longer if the hair is protected from the effects of atmospheric moisture, which will cause the hair to spring back to its original shape. Setting aids usually coat the hair with a soluble, water resistant coating, which will slow down the effects of atmospheric moisture on the hair. They also often contain ingredients which will help the hair to dry, and which help to reduce static electricity and make the hair controllable.

Setting lotions

These liquids often contain a thermoplastic, polyvinyl pyrollidone, which coats the hair with a film. This gradually breaks down with brushing and is washed away with shampooing. Setting lotions are available with a range of holding powers which offer from a strong hold through to a gentler, mild hold.

When selecting appropriate setting lotions you will often find that when setting fine, delicate hair you need a setting lotion which is not too heavy, but that when controlling strong hair you may need a stronger lotion. Setting lotions are usually applied to towel-dried hair, by sprinkling onto the hair direct from the bottle. When applying, gently massage the lotion; this will help to spread it and prevent it from running down the client's face and neck. Spread the application throughout the head, combing to ensure even distribution.

Points to remember

l Hair sets best when the hair has been shampooed.

l The hair set will last longer and be easier to dress if it follows the direction of hair growth.

l The set will last longer if protected from atmospheric moisture. Setting lotions can do this.

SETTING TECHNIQUES

The three setting techniques are:
l roller setting (winding)

l pin curling

l finger waving.

These three techniques may be used independently or in conjunction with each other to achieve different effects in the hair.

Roller setting (winding)

The placement of rollers usually follows the direction in which the root area of the hairstyle moves. The hair should be long enough to be wrapped around the roller at least $2\frac{1}{2}$ times. This will ensure that it will holds firmly in place.

To ensure maximum root movement and control over the hair the roller section should be the same size as the roller to be used. Remember that the size of roller used will determine the strength of curl and degree of root lift achieved.

TIP: As the hair retains the shape in which it is set, any misshapen or distorted ends will also be retained in the finished hairstyle.

 Shampooing and conditioning the hair and scalp, pages 27–38

Drying hair into shape, pages 39–50

Figure 11.4 Placing rollers

Using a comb, take a mesh of hair and comb away from the scalp so that the front of the mesh is at slightly more than 90 degrees to the scalp (see Figures 11.4 and 11.5). Hold the hair firmly and place the roller against the mesh (see Figure 11.6) near the point ends. The mesh of hair should be held centrally but without the points bunched together. Smooth the hair point ends around the roller (see Figure 11.7).

When using rollers with spikes, rotating the roller against the hair can help to ensure a smooth wrap for the hair ends. With the hair point ends wrapped smoothly around the roller, wind the roller down towards the scalp with the hair around it, without bunching. Allow the hair to spread across the width of the roller and ensure that there are no distortions in the hair as it is wrapped (see Figure 11.8).

Figure 11.5 Roller set for full volume

Figure 11.6 Placing roller against mesh

Figure 11.7 Smoothing hair point ends against roller

Figure 11.8 Winding roller towards scalp with hair on it

The angle at which the hair is held when the roller is placed at the ends can vary the degree of lift achieved in the finished style. Over-directing the mesh away from the direction of the style (see Figure 11.9), allows the hair to be controlled further towards the root, and is ideal when working on very curly hair.

Holding the mesh of hair at less that 90 degrees will flatten the root area (see Figures 11.10 and 11.11). This technique may be used when setting overly thick hair to reduce volume without thinning. In cases when no root lift is required at all, the hair may be combed flat to the head, and the roller may be placed on top of the mesh and wound back towards the root area (see Figure 11.12). This technique may be alternated with that in Figure 11.5 to produce deep wave movement at the scalp on long hair.

TIP: Buckled hair point ends or distorted hair lengths will not dress smoothly into the finished hairstyle.

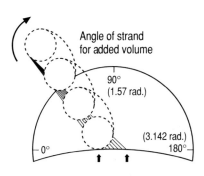

Figure 11.9 Overdirecting for added volume

Figure 11.10 Medium volume

Figure 11.11 Less volume

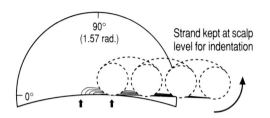

Figure 11.12 Strand curled at scalp level

Figure 11.13 Placing fixing pin

Features of good practice

- Never take sections with too much hair as this will extend the drying time and relax the curl strength towards the roots.
- For control roller sections should be no wider than the roller being used.
- Ensure that all the hair is wrapped with even tension, across the width of the curler.
- Spread the hair across the width of the roller as it winds.
- Avoid damaging or distorting the hair when placing the fixing pin (see Figure 11.13).

Pin curl setting

Pin curling enables you to place curled hair in the exact position, with the exact degree of curl and with the exact direction of root movement required for the finished dressing. There are three types of pin curls:

- barrel pin curls – a constant degree of curl throughout the length of hair (see Figure 11.14)
- stand up barrel curls – the same effect as that of a hair roller (see Figure 11.15)
- clock spring pin curl – a curl which gets tighter towards the hair points (see Figure 11.16).

Other than the 'stand up' curl, all others produce little or no root lift. There are three parts to the pin curl: the stem, the body and the base (see Figure 11.17).

The stem direction will determine the direction in which the hair moves, and will normally be determined by the required hairstyle. The size and direction of the body of the curl will determine the degree of movement and how the hair moves from the stem. The size and shape of the base will be determined by the required hairstyle, the thickness of the hair and the direction of the stem.

Figure 11.14 Barrel pin curls

Figure 11.15 Stand up barrel curls

Figure 11.16 Clock spring pin curl

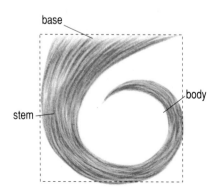

Figure 11.17 Parts of a curl

Figure 11.18 Forming barrel curls

Barrel curls

Take a section of hair and comb to remove any tangles. Mould the stem of the curl in the required direction and, holding the hair mesh at the point where the stem joins the curl body, form a rounded curl shape of the required size (see Figure 11.18).

Ensure that all of the hair is smoothly moulded into place and then secure the curl, locating a curl clip over the curl body. Place the clip over only as much of the curl body as is necessary to hold the curl. This will avoid unnecessary pressure marks on the hair (see Figure 11.19). When locating the clip avoid distortion of the stem and root area.

The stems may be directed to support the style, either with a long shaped stem (see Figure 11.20) to produce a flat, directed effect, or over-directed to deepen a movement (see Figure 11.21).

Figure 11.19 How to clip curls

Figure 11.20 Curling to produce a flat, directed effect

Figure 11.21 Overdirection for a deeper movement

Barrel curls may be used to produce a flat waved effect in hair, known as reverse pin curling. Rows of curls, placed with the body of the curl following the direction of the wave, may be dressed into a corresponding wave movement. The hair may first be moulded into a wave shape, and then the ends of the hair picked up and curled into the wave shape and secured (see Figure 11.22). Alternatively, section the hair into rows at the scalp and then subdivide the rows into pin curl sections. Pin curl the bodies of the curls for each row in alternate directions (see Figure 11.23).

Figure 11.22 Reverse pin curling

Figure 11.23 Reverse pin curling

Figure 11.24 Forming stand up barrel curls

Figure 11.25 Clip on stand up barrel curls

Figure 11.27 Clock spring curls

TIP: Apply lotion to one side of the head at a time; this prevents it from drying before completion and requiring additional applications.

Stand up barrel curls

Take sections of hair of a similar depth as that you would take for a hair roller, to produce a similar degree of curl. The width of the section should be no wider than the prongs of the securing clip. Hold the hair up from the scalp and comb to remove tangles and mould the hair together. As for hair rollers, the hair may be over-directed to gain maximum control of hold at less than 90 degrees to produce less root lift (see Figure 11.11).

Holding the points of the hair, create a rounded shape of the required size and rotate the hair until it rests at the scalp. Locate the securing clip through the curl onto the base of the section. Take care not to mark or indent the curl stem (see Figures 11.24 and 11.25).

Figure 11.26 Combined effects of barrel curls

Barrel curls may be produced which combine aspects of both the flat and the stand-up effects. This give subtle degrees of lift where a full effect may not be required (see Figure 11.26).

Clock spring curls

Clock spring curls are produced in a similar way to barrel curls, but the body of the curl is generally tighter, with the curl getting tighter towards the ends (see Figure 11.27). This type of curl is little used in modern hairstyling.

Finger waving

Finger waving is the technique of moulding and shaping the hair into wave movements using just fingers, comb, waving lotion and hairpins, clips or tape.

Apply waving lotion to towel-dried hair. Use an applicator bottle to apply the waving lotion and comb through to distribute. This allows the lotion to be distributed smoothly and evenly. Do not use an excessive amount of waving lotion as this may run onto the client's face and neck, causing them discomfort.

To determine the natural hair growth, comb the hair off the face, and push hair forward gently with the palm of your hand; the hair will fall into its natural growth pattern.

Shaping the top area

Using the first finger of your left hand as a guide, shape the top hair with a comb, using a circular movement. Starting at the front hairline, work towards the crown in 3.7 to 5 cm sections at a time until the crown has been reached (see Figure 11.28).

Place the first finger of the left hand directly above the position for the first crest. With the teeth of the comb pointing slightly upward, insert the comb directly under the first finger. Draw the comb forward about 2.5 cm along the fingertip (see Figure 11.29). With the teeth still inserted in the crest, flatten the comb against the head in order to hold the ridge in place (see Figure 11.30). Remove the left hand from the head, place the middle finger above the crest and the first finger on the teeth of the comb. Raise the crest by closing the two fingers and applying pressure to the head (see Figure 11.31).

Figure 11.28 Shaping the top area

Figure 11.29 Draw hair towards fingertip

Figure 11.30 Flatten comb against head

Without removing the comb, turn the teeth downward, and comb the hair in a right semi-circular direction to form a dip or trough in the hollow part of the wave (see Figure 11.32). Follow this procedure, section by section, until the crown you reach, where the crest phases out (see Figure 11.33).

Figure 11.31 Emphasize ridge

Figure 11.32 Comb hair in semi-circular direction

Figure 11.33 Complete first ridge at the crown

The crest and wave of each section should match evenly, without showing separations in the crest and trough part of the wave.

Forming the second crest

Start at the crown area (see Figure 11.34). The movements are the reverse of those followed in forming the first crest. The comb is drawn from the tip of the first finger towards its base, thus directing formation of the second ridge. All movements are followed in a reverse pattern until the hairline is reached, therefore completing the second crest, (see Figure 11.35).

Forming the third crest

Movements for the third crest closely follow those used in creating the first crest. However, the third ridge is started at the hairline and extended back toward the back of the head, (see Figure 11.36). Continue alternating directions until the side of the head has been completed, (see Figure 11.37).

195

Figure 11.34 Starting the second ridge

Figure 11.35 Complete second ridge

Figure 11.36 Start the third ridge

Figure 11.37 Complete right side

Figure 11.38 Setting net in place

🔊 TIP: For some fashion styling
techniques, once the setting tools
are removed the hair is combed
using only the stylist's fingers.
This retains the separate effect
on the curl. 🔊

Completion

Continue to create these wave movements around the head. The ends of
the hair may require pin curling if the hair is too long for you to mould into
the nape or onto the side of the face. The waves may be held in place while
you are drying them by placing setting tape along the wave troughs or
using clips or fine hair pins. Place a net over the hair, taking care not to
allow the net to press onto the hair, particularly on the front or on the
nape, as this will result in marks on the finished hairstyle. Dry the hair
thoroughly, using a hood hairdryer. Once dry remove your client from the
dryer, remove the net and any pins or clips and allow the hair to cool. Using
a bristle brush, brush the hair in the direction of the style. Dressing creams
or wax may be applied to the hair (to give control) and then using a
dressing comb reform the waves as they were set. Use the dressing mirror
to check the balance of your hairstyle.

DRYING THE HAIR

Always pre-heat the hairdryer. This will speed up the drying process as well
as making it more comfortable for your client. If required, place a setting
net over the hair set. Secure this ensuring that the net does not press onto
any area of the set, as this may mark the set and affect the finished dressing
(see Figure 11.38).

Check that no pins or metal items are pressing onto your client's scalp or
hairline. If they are, remove them or place a protective pad between the
tool and the scalp. Locate the hood of the dryer over the scalp area,
ensuring that all of the scalp area is enclosed without it resting on your
client's neck or on their face. Inform your client of how to regulate the heat
setting and set the timer for the desired time.

Avoid over-drying the hair as this can unnecessarily damage it. However,
the hair must be thoroughly dry if it is to be dressed satisfactorily. Allow the
hair set to cool slightly, before removing the rollers and pins. While the hair
is hot the shape may be relaxed.

Having removed the setting tools, brush the hair thoroughly in the
direction of the intended style, using a bristle brush.

DRESSING HAIR

Hair must be thoroughly dry when dressing into style. You may be dressing
hair following a wet set or you may be dressing hair which has been set
using heated rollers or you may be dressing hair which has little remaining
set. It is a distinct advantage to have some set in the hair as this will give
you control over the hair.

196

Thoroughly brush the hair, using a bristle brush, following the direction of the intended hairstyle. Care may be necessary when initially brushing the hair, not to cause discomfort when breaking down the crisp effect created by the use of a setting lotion (on freshly set hair) or the effects of hair-fixing spray and tangle (from previously set and dressed hair).

Hair may be moulded into shape using a bristle brush or a wide-toothed comb. Follow these guidelines:

▮ To achieve control, brush the hair holding the brush flat to the head.

▮ To achieve volume, slowly lift the brush or comb from the head allowing the hair to fall from the bristles (see Figure 11.39).

▮ To achieve curve under, place the brush under the section of hair and draw the hair in rolling under (see Figure 11.40).

▮ To achieve wave, use a comb or brush incorporating a finger wave technique (see Figure 11.41).

TIP: For control, use a dressing cream, oil or wax to control the hair and add shine.

Figure 11.39 Using brush or comb to achieve volume

Figure 11.40 Using brush or comb to achieve curve under

Figure 11.41 Using brush or comb to achieve wave

Back combing

Control and volume may be achieved in hair by back combing. Hair that has been tapered or has a natural taper can be back combed more easily. When building a hairstyle, just as when building a house, build from the bottom up. Use a comb with both widely- and closely-set teeth; there are specialised combs made with alternate longer and shorter teeth to aid back combing.

Take a mesh of hair, sufficiently small to be able to hold firmly, and grip towards the points using the first and second finger (see Figure 11.42). The thumb pressing onto the side of the first finger provides added grip. Comb and hold the hair at the angle you wish it to lie; so if you want height, hold the hair in an upright position, and if you want control and flatness hold the hair closer to the head.

Insert the comb, approximately one-third of the length out from the root, into the mesh and push down towards the root (see Figure 11.43). Some of the hair will matt. Continue to do this until the required degree of back combing is achieved, gradually extending the start position further from the hair root area.

When one section has been back combed take an adjacent section and continue. Stagger the section like the bricks in a wall. This will help to prevent gaps and partings in the finished dressing.

Some stylists back comb all or at least an area of the head before then using the wide teeth of the comb or a hair brush to dress the surface of the hair (see Figure 11.44). Others dress each mesh of hair in turn.

The surface of the hair is smoothed while the back combing is retained beneath.

Figure 11.42 Taking mesh for back combing

TIP: When dressing hair, check the balance of the style using the dressing mirror.

197

13 Shaving and face massage

This section provides the relevant essential knowledge about preparing for and carrying out a wet face shave and a facial massage. This includes the procedure for a complete facial shave and an outline shave, and will enable you to select appropriate tools and products and be aware of the correct procedure for carrying the process out safely.

CONTENTS

INTRODUCTION

The traditional art of the barber includes shaving and face massage. Evidence of shaving the beard may be found in the earliest civilisations. To many, these may appear to be skills that are no longer relevant, but they are undergoing a renaissance. Wet shaving is a skill which is still in demand in certain communities and geographic areas. Fashions in facial hair require the skill of outline shaving as part of the shaping process. The skills of shaving may also be applied to the art of shaved partings, used with Afro-Caribbean hair, to define a parting in short hair. Shaved outlines, used to define the hairline in sculptured designs around the ears and in the nape area, as well as shapes shaved in the hairlines, all require control in the execution to produce the finish required. Facial massage is usually coupled with the shaving process. It is a traditional barbering skill which may be used to relax your client and give him a feeling of well being.

FACIAL SHAVING
Tools and materials
Tools
Razors

The traditional tool for wet shaving is the open razor, a solid blade of metal pivoting from a handle or shield. The blade of the razor can be made of metal of varying hardness and with one of three cross-sectional shapes (or 'grinds'). The grinds are solid or wedge ground (see Figure 13.1), half-hollow ground (see Figure 13.2) and hollow ground.

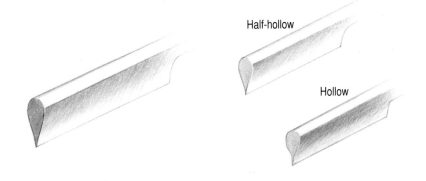

Figure 13.1 Solid ground razor   Figure 13.2 Half-hollow ground razor

The solid grind is the earliest shape and produced a rather heavy razor which could be difficult to manipulate and gave little sensation to the shaver, therefore making it difficult to determine the appropriate shaving pressure to be used. The half-hollow grind (or French) razor gave a little more sensitivity to the shaver. Traditionally made of a soft metal which made it easier to keep sharp but did not retain the edge, this razor was traditionally used for hair cutting and for shaving fine, delicate beards. The hollow ground (or German) razor was most widely used for shaving. Made of a very hard steel, which once sharp retained its edge, the finesse of the blade made it responsive to the shaver and easily manipulated across the face.

These 'fixed blade' open razors require frequent attention to the cutting edge. Immediately following use (to cleanse and dry the cutting edge) and immediately before each use (to polish and smooth the cutting edge) this type of razor requires stropping. Stropping is the process of drawing the cutting edge across a surface, usually leather. There are two types of strop, hanging and solid. The hanging strop is a flexible length of leather attached to a firm hook on the hydraulic chair and held taut at the other end. The leather surface is dressed (to aid its polishing action) with a sweet oil, and the razor is drawn along its length. Some strops also have a canvas surface which is dressed with a hard soap. This surface is used when the razor's edge becomes too dull or blunt for shaving, A hand, Hamon or solid strop is also available. This has a leather surface fixed to a sprung wooden strip. One end is rested on a firm surface and the other held raised by the hand. The surface of the leather is dressed with a specialised stropping paste. Some solid strops also have a surface of balsa wood.

When a razor becomes blunt it requires sharpening. This is accomplished using a hone. This is a slab of stone, either natural or reconstituted, lubricated by water or oil, which improves its bite or ability to sharpen, and the razor's cutting edge is pushed across its surface. Care must be taken to produce an edge which is even both in shape and sharpness.

Figure 13.3 Types of razor

To test the sharpness of a razor of this type, the cutting edge should be drawn very carefully across the line of the blade over a moistened thumb nail or the moistened end of the thumb. A dragging sensation indicates a sharp edge, a smooth sliding action indicates that the edge is not yet sharp. An uneven edge may appear sharp at some points and blunt at others. The use of a blunt razor will cause considerable client discomfort as well as causing extreme difficulty in hair removal.

To avoid cross infection razors should be washed after every use in hot soapy water, dried and then sterilised.

For commercial shaving these razors are no longer considered hygienically suitable. The difficulty in sterilising the edges of the blades made them unsuitable for use when there was a risk of puncturing the skin's surface. They are and may still be used safely when used only on one person. For all commercial wet shaving a razor which accepts a disposable blade must be used. There are a number of these commercially available (see Figure 13.3); they consist of a holder for the blade together with a handle/shield. Some styles accept a double edged blade, snapped in half, and others accept specially prepared blades which are fitted from a dispenser. There are also disposable razors available which are made in the style of the open razor.

Your choice of razor may depend on your salon policy or your personal preference.

Lather brushes
The best quality lather brushes are said to have bristles of badger hair. There are brushes available made of both natural and synthetic bristles.

Lather bowls
Clean, sterile bowls are required, one to contain a supply of very hot water in which to warm the lather brush, the second to contain the lather.

Materials
Shaving soap
The solid block form of soap must not be used when shaving commercially as the lather brush is placed on the face, then placed onto the shaving soap and then onto another client's face, facilitating the spread of infection from one client to the next. Powdered shaving soap may be shaken directly onto the bristles of a hot moist lather brush and then applied direct to the face and progressively worked up into a lather, but shaving cream or gel is the more up-to-date product. A small amount is placed into a bowl and then worked into a lather using the lather brush. Aerosol shaving foam is not suitable as working this lather decreases its foam.

Astringent

An astringent is a substance which closes the pores and tightens the skin. Cold water may be used as a mild astringent, or after-shave may be used. Take care as the perfume in the lotion may conflict with the cologne used by your client. The stinging effect of after-shave may be reduced by diluting it with water. This is particularly advisable when treating delicate skin. Witch hazel may also be used.

Fine talc

This is used to soothe the skin. The talc should be unperfumed so that it does not clash with your client's cologne.

Coagulant

In case of bleeding, a sterile coagulant such as powdered Alum BP or Ferric Chloride is required.

The shaving process

The shaving process breaks down into a number of steps:

1. preparation of the work area and tools
2. analysis of the beard area
3. preparing the face and softening the beard
4. removing the beard (first time over)
5. re-lathering the beard
6. removing the beard (second time over)
7. removing remaining lather
8. closing the pores
9. cleansing and sterilising tools and materials.

Preparation

Prepare all tools prior to undertaking the shave on your client. All tools that will make contact with your client's skin must be clean and sterile. An autoclave may be used to sterilise all metal tools; chemical sterilising fluids should be used to sterilise those tools which have parts that cannot stand high temperatures.

Check that the hydraulic chair is clean and safe for use. Lock the chair in position at its lowest level, with the back upright and head rest in place. Should your client step onto a hydraulic chair footrest when it is not locked in position, the chair may spin away from your client, causing them to fall. This type of chair is at its most stable when the hydraulic lift is at its lowest position, so this is the best position for it to be at when the client sits down. Raise the hydraulic chair to a comfortable working height using the pump, which may be foot-powered or electric. Remember to lock the swivel of the chair in place at all times when adjustment has been completed.

A number of hot steam towels will be required and should be prepared beforehand. Specialist towel steamers are available (see Figure 13.4).

Fold a towel in half, lengthwise, and then in half across the length. Apply a small amount of water to this fold, then roll the towel tightly from the fold towards the loose edges and wring it to spread the moisture through the towel. Place these prepared towels on the shelf in the towel steamer. They will require approximately 20 minutes to heat through. Avoid over-wetting the towel prior to steaming as excessive moisture can scald your client. The case of the towel steamer can become very hot when in use, so inform colleagues and clients to avoid touching this.

TIP: The autoclave sterilises by steaming items, under pressure, at a temperature of 120 °C. Only use an autoclave if you have been trained in its use or by following the manufacturer's directions for safe use.

Figure 13.4 Towel steamer

REMEMBER: Do not use a razor or any other sharp tool near your client without first ensuring that there is adequate clear space around you to prevent other stylists obstructing the process.

HEALTH AND SAFETY: Ensure that your hands are clean and that any open sores or cuts on your hands are covered with a waterproof dressing.

Preparing your client

Gown your client, using the cutting cloth – a square sheet with a cut midway along one side. Ensure that your client's clothing is fully protected, draw the cloth up around the client's neck and tuck into the collar (see Figure 13.5).

Always use a clean gown for each client, as this will help to reduce the possible spread of infection from one client to the next. Locate a clean, lightly coloured towel diagonally around the front of your client (see Figure 13.6), tucking the edges into the collar to protect your client's clothing. The use of a lightly coloured towel will reflect light onto the underside of the chin area.

Figure 13.5 Client gowned for a shave

Figure 13.6 White towel round client

Figure 13.7 Offering hot towel to face

Discuss the shaving process with your client, and establish the direction of beard growth by drawing your hands over the beard area. In one direction the beard will feel smooth and in the other the beard will feel at its roughest. The smooth feel will indicate that this is the direction of growth. This is usually in a downward direction on the face. There are, at times, conflicting directions of growth on the client's neck. Check the skin for any conditions which might prevent shaving, including open cuts and abrasions, muscular swelling, contagious skin disorders and pustular eruptions. The location of any unusual features such as moles etc. should be noted, as they will be less apparent once the lather is in place.

Place a clean towel or tissue over the headrest of the chair, ask your client to sit up and then recline the back of the chair to approximately 45 degrees before guiding your client back onto the chair's back, adjusting the headrest to ensure that your client's neck area is not over-stretched but exposed and lightly taut. Adjust the height of the chair so that your client's chin is at the level of your elbow. Apply a steam towel to the beard area to help to soften the beard and cleanse the skin. Protecting your hands from the steam using wooden tongs or a dry clean towel, remove a steam towel from the steamer. Wring out any excess moisture, taking care not to allow the hot water to run onto your hands. Unwrap the towel, taking care that the steam given off does not scald your skin. A towel which is too hot may be held without causing you pain by tossing the towel in your hands. This will also help it to cool more rapidly. With the towel still folded in half lengthways, stand at the back of the chair and offer the towel to your client's face (see Figure 13.7).

Allow the face to become accustomed to the heat and then wrap the towel loosely around the face, taking care to ensure that all of the beard area is covered, but that the ears do not become covered, as they are sensitive to heat. Gentle pressure onto the towel around the beard area will increase the conduction of heat to the face. Remove the towel before it becomes cool and lather the beard area. The bristles of the lather brush should be pre-heated using hot water. Build up the lather in the lather bowl and then, using a rotary action, apply the lather to the beard area (see Figure 13.8). You can achieve greater control of the lather by gripping the handle and the tops of the bristles. When lathering the top lip, you can achieve a finer spread of the brush through fanning the bristles: press the finger into the base of the bristles (see Figure 13.9).

Figure 13.8 Applying lather to beard area

Figure 13.9 Applying lather to top lip

Lather will soften the beard and help to support the bristles away from the face. Ensure that the face and lather is kept warm throughout the shaving process. To assist in softening the beard, a further steam towel may be applied over the top of the lather. Remove this steam towel before it becomes cold and then re-lather the beard area. Once the lather has built up, the shave may be carried out. A clean tissue or towel will be required to wipe the razor on during the shaving process.

The shave

Hold the razor with the first two or three fingers and thumb on the shaft and the remainder on the tang. At all times the razor should be held firmly, with dry hands, so that it may be manipulated from freehand and back hand positions (see Figure 13.10).

The movement of the razor is driven from the wrist. Stretch the skin taut, either behind or in front of the razor: stretching the skin in front of the razor will give a more comfortable, less close shave; stretching behind the razor will give the reverse. If necessary remove lather from the face so that the skin may be stretched more effectively. Lay the razor on the skin, tilting the back of the razor away from the skin at approximately 30 degrees, and firmly but gently draw the razor across the beard. The shaving stroke must move the blade through the beard, avoid using a slicing action which will cut the skin. The shaving stroke is a smooth action extending only as far as the skin is taut. When shaving it is normal to shave positioned to the right-hand side of the client and at the back.

Should your client be cut while shaving, apply a small amount of powdered Alum, a powdered styptic, from a sterile dressing. Ferric chloride may be used as a liquid styptic. Never use an Alum stick, as it may be used on more that one client, and there may be a risk of spreading blood-related disorders.

Careful tensioning of the skin and correct movement of the razor considerably reduces the risk of cutting your client. Take care when shaving over curved surfaces of the face, for example the chin, as it is easy to shave too close and cause short-term bleeding.

Figure 13.10 Holding the open razor

NOTE: Never undertake a shaving stroke without the client's skin being held taut.

HEALTH AND SAFETY: Do not leave an open razor lying unclosed when not in use as there is a risk of someone accidentally cutting themselves.

First time over shave

The first time over shaving strokes, in the main, follow the direction of beard growth.

1. Standing to the side of your client, with your client's face turned away from you and starting at the lower edge of the sideburn, stretch the skin and shave using a freehand movement, to the corner of the jaw.

2. Follow this with a backhand movement across the cheek. The exact start point for this movement will be determined by the extent of beard growth.

3. Stretching the skin upwards, shave freehand along the jawbone. By stretching up, the jawbone will be free of hair, once released.

4. Stretching both upwards and downwards, shave the under-jaw area using a freehand movement.

5. Turn your client's face towards you, and use a backhand movement to shave from the sideburn down to the corner of the jaw on the other side of the face.

6. This is followed by a freehand movement across the cheek.

7. Stretch the skin upwards and shave, freehand, along the jawbone.

8. Standing slightly forward of your client stretch the under-jaw area, both upwards and downwards and shave the area backhand. This area may require more than one stroke.

9. Move your client's face to a central position. Apply fresh lather, if required.

10. Using a freehand movement and stretching either side of the chin and upwards, shave across the chin area. Take care not to shave too close as this may cause bleeding.

Figures 13.12–15 Basic first time over strokes

1 = Freehand
2 = Backhand
3 = Freehand
4 = Freehand
5 = Backhand
6 = Freehand
7 = Freehand
8 = Backhand
9 = Freehand
10 = Freehand
11 = Freehand
12 = Freehand reverse
13 = Freehand
14 = Backhand
15 = Freehand

Figure 13.11 First-time over shaving strokes

11. Standing slightly to the front of your client, shave freehand down the centre under-jaw area.

12. Return to the side of your client and shave the upper chin area using a freehand movement, taking care not to draw the razor's point along the crease of the chin, below the lip.

13. Shave the area from the lip down to the crease of the skin, using a freehand movement, stretching the skin to either side of the mouth.

14. Shave the top lip freehand down the centre, then shave the near side freehand and the far side backhand in an outward/downward direction.

As the razor's blade becomes clogged or coated with lather and removed beard, wipe the blade by laying it flat on the tissue or towel placed on your client's shoulder for this purpose, and drawing it across the towel with the razor's back leading. Never attempt a shaving movement when the razor's edge cannot be clearly seen.

Second time over shave

These movements will remove the remaining beard, giving a closer shave. The shaving stroke will, in the main, go against or across the direction of beard growth. More resistance to the razor will be experienced and firm but gentle movements must be used to overcome this without causing your client discomfort. Re-lather the beard, using fresh supplies of lather and hot water. Once the lather has built up the shave may commence.

1. direct your client's face away from you, and starting from the hairline on the neck on the left side of your client, stretch down on the neck and shave upwards towards the jawbone using a reverse backhand stroke.

2. The next reverse backhand stroke is used diagonally upwards across the jaw, stretching the skin in front of the razor.

TIP: Do not attempt to shave the skin without a lubricant on the surface.

Figure 13.16 Second time over shaving strokes

1 = Backhand reverse
2 = Backhand reverse
3 = Backhand reverse
4 = Backhand
5 = Freehand
6 = Freehand
7 = Freehand
8 = Freehand reverse
9 = Freehand reverse
10 = Freehand
11 = Backhand reverse
12 = Freehand reverse
13 = Freehand
14 = Freehand
15 = Backhand diagonal

3. This is followed by a reverse backhand movement from the corner of the jawbone upwards towards the sideburn stretching downwards on the skin.

4. A backhand movement follows diagonally across the cheek area, as for the first time over.

5. Finally, on this side of the face, a backhand movement is used towards the chin along the jawbone in the chin area, stretching the skin back towards the corner of the jaw.

6. Move your client's face to face towards you. Standing slightly forward at the side of your client, start at the hairline and use a reverse freehand stroke at the neck, stretching the skin down on the neck.

7. Move behind your client, and reaching over him, using a reverse freehand movement shave from the corner of the jaw towards the sideburn, stretching the skin taut downwards behind the razor.

8. Moving back to the side of the client, shave across the cheek area using a freehand movement, stretching the skin behind. Stretching the skin upwards and back towards the client's ear, use a freehand movement to shave across the area of the jawbone.

9. With your client's face in the central position, and standing forward of the side of your client, use a reverse backhand movement to shave the central area under the chin, stretching downwards and out to each side.

10. Stretch the skin across the chin, pulling this area upwards as well, and shave across the chin using a freehand stroke.

11. Standing at the back of your client and reaching over him, stretch the chin area downwards and using a freehand movement shave the area between the crease of the chin and the bottom lip.

12. Move to the side of your client, shave the centre of the top lip in a downward direction, stretching the skin towards either side.

13. Stretch the nearest side of the top lip outwards and shave with a backhand movement towards the middle. Stretch the furthest side of the top lip outwards and shave towards the centre using a freehand movement. Remove the towel or tissue used to wipe the razor free of lather and beard hair and dispose of it hygienically.

Following the completion of the shave a further hot towel is applied to your client's beard area. This should be removed from the face before cooling and then carefully wrapped around your hand and used to wipe any remaining lather from the face. Pay particular attention to the ear, nose and collar areas.

Having removed the hot towel, apply a cold towel to close the pores, preventing infection and aiding retraction of the facial hair. Allow the cold towel to remain on the face for a few moments, using hand pressure to increase the conductivity of the cooling effect. A cold towel may be prepared in the same manner as a hot towel, using cold water and mild refrigeration to cool. This may be followed by the application of a mild astringent or after-shave which will also close the pores and tighten the skin. When applying astringent, place a small amount on one hand, work this onto both hands and then using brisk, gentle slapping strokes apply this to the beard area, taking care not to be over-generous or to apply to the areas around the eyes.

Fold a tissue onto your hand and use this to pat the surface of the skin dry before applying unperfumed talc, to soothe and remove shine from the skin. When applying talc to the face, place a small amount onto the hands and apply directly to the beard area or using a talc puffer. Shield your client's eyes and apply directly to the face.

Figure 13.17–13.20 Second time over shaving strokes

HEALTH AND SAFETY: Never leave an open razor unclosed.

Figure 13.35 Vibro massager in use on side of nose

Prepare the client and his face as for the facial massage already described. Firmly attach the bell-shaped applicator to the massager. Due to the delicate nature of the facial skin, the vibro-massager must be used gently on the skin. Avoid pressure on areas where the jaw bone etc. are prominent.

1. Use circular movements across the upper jaw area.

2. Draw the vibro across the neck in sweeping motions either side of the windpipe.

3. Supporting the side of the nose with your free hand, gently draw the vibro along the side of the nose from the tip up towards the forehead. Take care that the applicator does not jar on any prominent bone or cartilage.

4. Place the applicator on the back of your free hand and massage the muscle around the eyes using the fingers of this hand.

Finish and tidy away material as described previously. Remember to wipe the casing of the vibro massager and to wash, dry and sterilise the applicator.

FURTHER STUDY

See information about bye-laws in chapter 10 'Health, safety and security in the salon', pages 179–185

▮ To obtain best results from facial massage, you must have a thorough knowledge of all the structures involved: muscles, nerves and blood vessels. Find out more about them.

▮ Every muscle and nerve has a motor point. In order to obtain the maximum benefits from a facial massage you must consider the motor nerve points that affect the underlying muscles of the face and neck.

▮ Local bye-laws may regulate the offering of barbering skills. Find out from your local area what these bye-laws require.

Review questions

1. State two circumstances which may prevent you from carrying out a wet shave.

2. What steps should be taken should your client's skin be cut while shaving?

3. Suggest two reasons for stretching the skin while shaving.

4. What benefit is gained by the use of steam towels?

5. What is the purpose of astringent lotions applied to the skin following a wet shave?

6. What directions should the first time over shaving strokes follow?

7. How should 'sharps' be disposed of?

8. What benefit is obtained by shaving the nape hairline?

9. What benefits, for your client, are achieved by facial massage?

10. What is the purpose of using cold towels following a facial massage?

14 | The hair and scalp

This section will give you the essential knowledge about the structure and properties of the hair, scalp and skin. This section will also help you to identify hair, scalp and skin disorders and to be aware of those that may preclude hairdressing processes and those that do not.

Out

Inn

Cor

Mec

Cut

Inne

Out

Level 1

Unit 6
Element 6.1 - Maintain personal
  health, hygiene and appearance

Level 2

Unit 1
Element 1.1 - Consult with client on
  technical services and products

Unit 2
Element 2.1 - Shampoo and surface
  condition hair and scalp

Element 2.2 - Apply conditioning
  treatment to hair and scalp

Unit 10
Element 10.1 - Maintain personal
  health, hygiene and appearance

Unit 13
Element 13.1 - Remove hair by shaving

CONTENTS

T
an
nat
T
of tl
and
T
hair
in tl
hair
long
enal

Stru

Arre
The
und
stan
and

Seba
Thes
conn
beco
form

Figure 14.16 Alopecia areata

Figure 14.17 Tinea capitis

Figure 14.18 Tinea favosa (honeycomb ringworm)

frequently in spring and autumn. Hair loss due to alopecia is not replaced unless special treatments are given to encourage hair growth. Hairstyles such as ponytails and tight braids cause tension on the hair and can contribute to constant hair loss or baldness.

Alopecia senilis is the form of baldness that occurs in old age. This loss of hair is permanent. It is not contagious.

Alopecia prematura is the form of baldness that begins any time before middle age with a slow, thinning process. This condition is caused when hairs fall out and are replaced by weaker ones. It is not contagious.

Alopecia areata is the sudden falling out of hair in round patches, or baldness in spots, sometimes caused by anaemia, scarlet fever, typhoid fever or syphilis. Patches are round or irregular in shape and can vary in size from 1.25 to 5 or 7.5 cm (1/2" to 2" or 3") in diameter. Affected areas are slightly depressed, smooth and very pale due to a decreased blood supply. In most conditions of alopecia areata, the nervous system has been subjected to some injury. Since the flow of blood is influenced by the nervous system, the affected area also is poorly nourished (see Figure 14.16).

Treatment for alopecia

Alopecia appears in a variety of different forms, caused by many abnormal conditions. Sometimes an alopecia condition can be improved by proper scalp treatments.

Infections

All the infections covered below are contagious.

Vegetable parasitic infections

Tinea is the medical term for ringworm. Ringworm is caused by vegetable parasites. All forms are contagious and can be transmitted from one person to another. The disease is commonly carried by scales or hairs containing fungi. Bathtubs, swimming pools and unsterilised articles are also sources of transmissions.

Ringworm starts with a small, reddened patch of little blisters. Several such patches may be present. Any ringworm condition should be referred to a medical practitioner.

Tinea capitis, ringworm of the scalp, is characterised by red papules, or spots, at the opening of the hair follicles (see Figure 14.17). The patches spread and the hair becomes brittle and lifeless. It breaks off, leaving a stump, or falls from the enlarged open follicles.

Tinea favosa, also *favus* or *honeycomb ringworm* is characterised by dry sulphur yellow cuplike crusts on the scalp, called **scutula**, which have a peculiar odour (see Figure 14.18). Scars from favus are bald patches that may be pink or white and shiny. It is very contagious and should be referred to a medical practitioner.

Animal parasitic infections

Scabies 'itch' is a highly contagious, animal parasitic skin disease, caused by the itch mite. Vesicles and pustules can form from the irritation of the parasites or from scratching the affected areas.

Pediculosis capitis is a contagious condition caused by the *head louse* (animal parasite) infesting the hair of the scalp (see Figure 14.19). The adult female is 3–4 mm long, the male slightly smaller. The female adult, during their life span of approximately one month, lays 7–10 eggs per day. The eggs hatch in about 8 days and the louse becomes sexually mature within a further 8 days.

As the parasites feed on blood at the scalp, itching occurs and the resultant scratching can cause infection. The head louse is transmitted from one person to another by contact with infested hats, combs, brushes or other personal articles. To kill head lice advise the client to apply a proprietary brand of treatment, following the manufacturer's instructions. Proprietary brands of treatment shampoo may be used to remove the infestation. However, to prevent re-infestation usually the application of a treatment lotion is required. The duration of an infestation may be calculated by the position of the egg along the hair's length. The female adult lays its egg on the hair next to the scalp, therefore eggs located 1 cm from the scalp will have been produced one month previous. The unsightly husks of the 'nit' or egg may be removed using a fine toothed comb.

Staphylococci infections

A *furuncle* or boil is an acute staphylococci infection of a hair follicle that produces constant pain (see Figure 14.20). It is limited to a specific area and produces a pustule perforated by hair.

Figure 14.19 Pediculosis capitis

Figure 14.20 Furuncle, or boil

A *carbuncle* is the result of an acute staphylococci infection and is larger than a furuncle. Refer the client to a medical practitioner.

SKIN

The skin is the largest and one of the most important organs of the body. The scientific study of the skin and scalp is important to the hairdresser and beautician because it forms the basis for an effective programme of skin care, beauty services and scalp treatments. A hairdresser who has a thorough under-standing of skin, its structure and functions is in a better position to give clients professional advice on scalp, facial and hand care (see Figure 14.21).

A healthy skin is slightly moist, soft and flexible; posses a slightly acid reaction; and is free from any disease or disorder. The skin also has immunity responses to organisms that touch or try to enter it. Its texture (feel and appearance) ideally is smooth and fine grained. A person with a good complexion has fine skin texture and healthy skin colour. Appendages of the skin are hair, nails and sweat and oil glands.

Skin varies in thickness. It is thinnest on the eyelids and thickest on the palms and soles. Continued pressure on any part of the skin can cause it to thicken and develop a callus.

The skin of the scalp is constructed similarly to the skin elsewhere on the human body. However, the scalp has larger and deeper hair follicles to accommodate the longer hair of the head (see Figure 14.22).

Histology of the skin

The skin contains two main divisions: the epidermis and the dermis.

The *epidermis* is the outermost layer of the skin. It is the thinnest layer of

Figure 14.21 Microscopic section of skin

243

Lesions of the skin

A lesion is a structural change in the tissues caused by injury or disease. There are three types: primary, secondary and tertiary. The beautician is concerned with primary and secondary lesions only. If you are familiar with the principal skin lesions you will be able to distinguish between conditions that may or may not be treated in a salon (see Figure 14.26).

The symptoms or signs of diseases of the skin are divided into two groups:

I *Subjective symptoms* are those that can be felt, such as itching, burning or pain.

I *Objective symptoms* are those that are visible, such as pimples, pustules or inflammation.

Definitions about primary lesions

The following is a list of important terms and definitions that should be familiar to the beautician.

I *Macule.* A small, discoloured spot or patch on the surface of the skin, such as freckles. These are neither raised nor sunken.

I *Papule.* A small, elevated pimple on the skin, containing no fluid, but which might develop pus.

I *Wheal.* An itchy, swollen lesion that lasts only a few hours. Examples include hives, or the bite of an insect, such a mosquito.

I *Tubercle.* A solid lump larger than a papule. It projects above the surface or lies within or under the skin. It varies in size from a pea to a walnut.

I *Tumour.* An abnormal cell mass, varying in size, shape and colour. Nodules are also referred to as tumours, but they are smaller.

I *Vesicle.* A blister with clear fluid in it. Vesicles lie within or just beneath the epidermis; for example, poison ivy produces small vesicles.

I *Bulla.* A blister containing a watery fluid, similar to a vesicle, but larger.

I *Pustule.* An elevation of the skin having an inflamed base, containing pus.

I *Cyst.* A semi-solid or fluid lump above and below the skin.

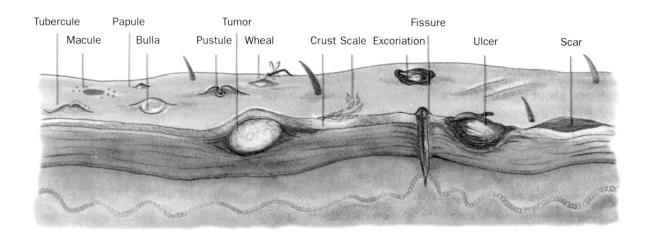

Figure 14.26 Primary and secondary skin lesions

Definitions about secondary lesions

Secondary skin lesions are those that develop in the later stages of disease. These are:

I *Scale.* An accumulation of epidermal flakes, dry or greasy. Example: abnormal or excessive dandruff.

l *Crust*. An accumulation of sebum and pus, mixed perhaps with epidermal material. Example: the scab on a sore.

l *Excoriation*. A skin sore or abrasion produced by scratching or scraping. Example: a raw surface due to the loss of the superficial skin after injury.

l *Fissure*. A crack in the skin penetrating into the dermis, as in the case of chapped hands or lips.

l *Ulcer*. An open lesion on the skin or mucous membrane of the body, accompanied by pus and loss of skin depth.

l *Scar*. Likely to form after the healing of an injury or skin condition that has penetrated the dermal layer.

l *Stain*. An abnormal discoloration remaining after the disappearance of moles, freckles or liver spots, sometimes apparent after certain diseases.

Definitions about disease

Before describing the disease of the skin and scalp so that they will be recognisable to the hairdresser/beautician, it is necessary to understand what is meant by disease.

l *Contagious disease*. One that is communicable by contact.

l *Disease*. Any departure from a normal state of health.

l *Skin disease*. Any infection of the skin characterised by an objective lesion (one that can be seen), which may consist of scales, pimples or pustules.

l *Acute disease*. One with symptoms of a more or less violent character such as fever and usually of short duration.

l *Chronic disease*. One of long duration, usually mild but recurring.

l *Infectious disease*. One due to germs (bacterial or viral) taken into the body as a result of contact with a contaminated object or lesion.

l *Congenital disease*. One that is present in the infant at birth.

l *Seasonal disease*. One that is influenced by the weather, as prickly heat in the summer, and forms of eczema, which is more prevalent in cold weather.

l *Occupational disease* (such as dermatitis). One that is due to certain kinds of employment, such as coming in contact with cosmetics, chemicals or tints.

l *Parasitic disease*. One that is caused by vegetable or animal parasites, such as pediculosis and ringworm.

l *Pathogenic disease*. One produced by disease-causing bacteria, such as staphylococcus and streptococcus (pus-forming bacteria), or viruses.

l *Systemic disease*. Due to under- or over-functioning of internal glands. It can be caused by faulty diet.

l *Venereal disease*. A contagious disease commonly acquired by contact with an infected person during sexual intercourse.

l *Epidemic*. The appearance of a disease that simultaneously attacks a large number of persons living in a particular locality. Infantile paralysis, influenza or smallpox are examples of epidemic-causing diseases.

l *Allergy*. A sensitivity that some people develop to normally harmless substances. Skin allergies are quite common. Contact with certain types of cosmetics, medicines and tints or eating certain foods all can cause an itching eruption, accompanied by redness, swelling, blisters, oozing and scaling.

NOTE: The terms 'infectious disease', 'communicable disease' and 'contagious disease' are often used interchangeably.

Figure 14.27 Blackheads

I *Inflammation.* A skin disorder characterised by redness, pain, swelling and heat.

Disorders of the sebaceous (oil) glands

There are several common disorders of the sebaceous (oil) glands that the hairdresser/beautician should be able to identify and understand.

Comedones, or blackheads, are wormlike masses of hardened sebum, appearing most frequently on the face, especially the forehead and nose.

Blackheads accompanied by pimples often occur in youths between the ages of 13 and 20. During this adolescent period, the activity of the sebaceous glands is stimulated, thereby contributing to the formation of blackheads and pimples (see Figure 14.27).

When the hair follicle is filled with an excess of oil from the sebaceous gland, a blackhead forms and creates a blockage at the moth of the follicle. Should this condition become severe, medical attention is necessary.

To treat blackheads, the skin's oiliness must be reduced by local applications of cleansers and the blackheads removed under sterile conditions. Thorough skin cleansing each night is a very important factor. Cleansing creams and lotions often achieve better results than common soap and water.

Milia, or whiteheads, is a disorder of the sebaceous (oil) glands caused by the accumulation of sebaceous matter beneath the skin. This can occur on any part of the face, neck and, occasionally, on the chest and shoulders. Whiteheads are associated with fine-textured, dry types of skin.

Acne is a chronic inflammatory disorder of the sebaceous glands, occurring most frequently on the face, back and chest. The cause of acne is generally believed to be microbic, but predisposing factors are adolescence and perhaps certain foods in the diet. Acne, or common pimples, is also known as *acne simplex* or *acne vulgaris* (see Figure 14.28).

Figure 14.28 *Acne simplex*, or *acne vulgaris*

Acne appears in a variety of different types, ranging from the simple (non contagious) pimple, to serious, deep-seated skin conditions. It is always advisable to have the condition examined and diagnosed by a medical practitioner before any service is given in a salon.

Seborrhea is a skin condition caused by an excessive secretion of the sebaceous glands. An oily or shiny condition of the nose, forehead or scalp indicates the presence of seborrhea. On the scalp, it is readily detected by an unusual amount of oil on the hair.

Asteatosis is a condition of dry, scaly skin, characterised by absolute or partial deficiency of sebum, due to senile changes (old age) or some bodily disorders. It can be caused by alkalis, such as those found in soaps and washing powders.

Rosacea, formerly called acne rosacea, is a chronic inflammatory congestion of the cheeks and nose. It is characterised by redness, dilation of the blood vessels and the formation of papules and pustules. The cause of rosacea is unknown. Certain things are known to aggravate rosacea in some individuals. These include consumption of hot liquids, spicy food or alcohol, being exposed to extremes of heat and cold, exposure to sunlight and stress.

Steatoma, or sebaceous cyst, is a subcutaneous tumour of the sebaceous gland. It is filled with sebum and ranges in size from a pea to an orange. It usually appears on the scalp, neck and back. A steatoma is sometimes called a wen.

Definitions about disorders of the sudoriferous (sweat) glands

Bromidrosis or *osmidrosis*. Foul-smelling perspiration, usually noticeable in the armpits or on the feet.

Anhidrosis, or lack of perspiration. Often a result of fever or certain skin diseases. It requires medical treatment.

Hyperhidrosis, or excessive perspiration. Caused by excessive heat or general body weakness. The most commonly affected parts are the armpits, joints and feet. Medical treatment is required.

Miliaria rubra, or *prickly heat*. An acute inflammatory disorder of the sweat glands, characterised by an eruption of small red vesicles and accompanied by burning and itching of the skin. It is caused by exposure to excessive heat.

Definitions about inflammations

Dermatitis. A term used to indicate an inflammatory condition of the skin. The lesions come in various forms, such as vesicles or papules.

Eczema. An inflammation of the skin, of acute or chronic nature, presenting many forms of dry or moist lesions. It is frequently accompanied by itching or a burning sensation. All cases of eczema should be referred to a medical practitioner for treatment. Its cause is unknown.

Psoriasis. A common, chronic, inflammatory skin disease whose cause is unknown. It is usually found on the scalp, elbows, knees, chest and lower back, rarely on the face. The lesions are round, dry patches covered with coarse, silvery scales. If irritated, bleeding points occur. It is not contagious.

Herpes simplex. A recurring virus infection, commonly called fever blisters. It is characterised by the eruption of a single vesicle or group of vesicles on a red swollen base. The blisters usually appear on the lips, nostrils or other parts of the face and rarely last more than a week. It is contagious (see Figure 14.29).

Figure 14.29 *Herpes simplex*, or cold sore

Occupational disorders in hairdressing

Abnormal conditions resulting from contact with chemicals or tints can occur in the course of performing services in the salon. Some individuals may develop allergies to ingredients in cosmetics, antiseptics, cold waving lotions and aniline derivative tints. These can cause eruptive skin infections known as *dermatitis venenata*. It is important that hairdressers employ protective measures, such as the use of rubber gloves or protective creams whenever possible.

Research in many countries has shown that between 10 – 50% of hairdressers (male and female) suffer from eczema. Hairdressers' eczema is caused when the skin comes in contact with:

I water

I chemicals including shampoo, hair bleaches and liquids used with permanent colouring

I nickel (in scissors, combs, blow dryers and money)

I air flows (blow dryers and wind).

Respiratory disorders may be produced by the inhalation of products such as bleach powder, hair sprays and permanent waves.

> **TIP: Your employer may have set in place procedures to follow when using certain chemicals. These procedures should reduce risk to an acceptable level.**

FURTHER STUDY

I Find out your salon's procedures for advising clients who may have a contagious scalp disorder.

I Find out who you should inform, within your salon, when encountering a contagious scalp disorder.

I Investigate which shampoos and lotions are available, and their methods of use, to recommend to clients in the treatment of *Pediculosis capitis*.

I Find out if your salon has guidelines in the safe use of chemicals such as perm lotion, powder bleach.

Review questions

1. What are infectious conditions?
2. How should you protect yourself from the effects of chemicals when working on clients?
3. What term is used for abnormal hair loss?
4. For how long does the female head louse live?
5. What is the most effective treatment for split ends in hair?
6. What is the period of hair growth known as?
7. Name the three areas of the hair root.
8. Name the three layers found in hair.
9. Name a fungal parasitic scalp disorder?
10. Name the term given to excessive production of sebum.

15 | Model answers

CHAPTER 1

1. Client's name (including initial), client's address, client's telephone number, the name of any products used on the hair, the costs.

2. To the manager/manageress.

3. Confused look on their face, lack of response, fidgeting.

4. By their surname (if known), introduce self and ask them their name, or sir or madam.

5. Contagious conditions including Pediculosis capititis (head lice), Tinea capititis (ringworm of the scalp). Recommend that they consult a medical practitioner.

6. Texture.

7. Porosity.

8. When wet.

9. Cowlick – strong upward movement at front hairline.

   Nape whorls – strong circular growth patterns at the nape area.

   Double crown – two strong circular conflicting growth pattern at the crown.

CHAPTER 2

1. A range of commercial or proprietary brand names and their related hair/scalp types.

2. Lime scale can form, blocking the jets.

3. When the client's hair cannot be made wet or when drying would be difficult.

4. On the back of the hand.

5. Circular movements using the pads of the fingers.

6. Zinc Pyrethione and Selenium Sulphide.

7. 4.5 to 5.5.

8. Coats the cuticle of the hair, making it feel smoother and less likely to tangle.

9. To even out the hair's porosity before perming

   To protect hair from the effect of chemicals.

10. Increased blood flow.

    Stimulation of the sebaceous gland.

    Client relaxation.

11. Deep kneading and gripping movement using the pads of the fingers.

12. Open cuts or sores on the scalp.

    Muscular swelling.

    Client experiencing discomfort.

13. Moist heat swells the hair shaft allowing the conditioner to penetrate more effectively.

14. Distilled or de-ionised water.

CHAPTER 3

1. Hydrogen bonds.

2. Golf ball size.

3. From a distance of at least 30 cm, avoid wet patches or spraying onto the client's face or neck.

4. Speed up elastic recoil, the set/blow dry will drop.

5. The required style, the hair type and the client's preference.

6. By blow drying into the root area of upheld meshes of hair. By drying the root area against the direction of the style.

7. By directing the air flow in the direction of the style.

8. The diffuser.

9. Styling wax.

10. Heavy, greasy appearance.

CHAPTER 4

1. Hair type, direction of hair growth, the length of the hair, client's personal preference.

2. To protect the client and their clothing from hair clippings.

3. With the thumb and third finger.

4. Club cutting.

5. Taper cutting and thinning.

6. Graduation.

7. An area where additional bulk is created by the volume of hair.

8. Drawing the fingers through meshes of hair from either side of the head and comparing, using the dressing point mirror or by drawing strands of hair from even points on each side, whose hair ends should meet in the middle.

9. The hair may be cut closer to the head than can be done with the hair held in the fingers.

10. Wet hair.

CHAPTER 5A

1. It provides the client with hairstyle options which otherwise would not be available.
2. The ability of hair to absorb moisture.
3. How thick or thin an individual hair is.
4. The ability of hair to be stretched and then return to its original length.
5. The number of hairs, on the scalp, per square centimetre.
6. Winding the hair spirally along the rod, usually from root to point.
7. Winding the hair around itself on the rod, from point to root.
8. a) Introduces hydrogen to the hair, which breaks down the disulphide bonds in the hair.

   b) Introduces oxygen to the hair, which removes the hydrogen, allowing the sulphur bonds to reform into disulphide bonds.
9. The degree or strength of curl required.
10. A pre-processed curl used to determine correct lotion choice.
11. Strength of lotion used.

    Hair type.
12. Slow down the processing or extend the processing time.
13. Hair lacking in elasticity, hair breakage.
14. Rapid drop of curl, uneven curl.
15. To remove the perm lotion from the hair.
16. Hydrogen peroxide.

CHAPTER 5B

1. Two chemicals often used in chemical hair relaxing products are sodium hydroxide and ammonium thioglycolate.
2. The term 'base' means, in relation to hair relaxation processes, a petroleum cream designed to protect the scalp during the straightening process.
3. The client's hairline and face should be protected during relaxing chemical processes, by the application to the complete hairline of barrier cream and moist cotton wool.
4. The three main stages of the chemical hair relaxation process are processing, neutralising and conditioning.
5. The strand test is used to determine the hair's porosity and elasticity.
6. The hairdresser should wear protective gloves when working with relaxing/straightening substances.
7. Straightener products should be applied no closer than 5 cm from the scalp.
8. The main stages of a two-step perm are rearrange the curl (straighten the hair), wind and curl the hair, neutralise the hair, condition the hair.
9. 'Over-directing' when curler winding, means to comb the hair upwards and away from the direction of the wind.
10. Little or no tension should be used when winding the hair during a two-step perm.

8. The possible consequences in not following accident, emergency and evacuation procedures, are injury to self or client and the possible neutralising of compensation rights.

9. Damaged equipment should be reported to the responsible person in the salon.

10. Failure to sweep up hair clippings from the floor may result in someone slipping and being injured.

CHAPTER 11

1. A set is retained in the hair until affected by moisture from the atmosphere or by shampooing.

2. The type of hair roller most likely to mark bleached or very porous hair is the spiked roller.

3. When roller setting, the curler diameter determines the strength of curl achieved.

4. The section taken should be the same as the size of roller to be used.

5. Hair in its unstretched state is known as alpha keratin.

6. The term 'over directing', when setting hair, means to direct the roots of the mesh of hair away from the direction of the set.

7. The hair should be brushed in the direction of the intended style prior to dressing.

8. Back combing should normally follow the direction of the hair style.

9. Always protect the client's face and neck when applying hair fixing spray.

10. Fine pins should be positioned in a downwards direction so that they do not fall out of the dressing.

CHAPTER 12

1. The electric clipper should be inverted to outline a beard.

2. The hydraulic chair should be locked in its lowest position when the client is invited to sit.

3. Light coloured towels are used when beard trimming to reflect light under the beard area and to give a contrast with the beard.

4. The largest size clipper grader available is 'number 8'.

5. A clean tissue placed on the chair's head rest while trimming the beard to reduce the risk of the spread of infection from one client to the next.

6. When beard trimming, the area beneath the chin will appear longer when the head is upright.

7. Scissor-over-comb techniques are used when a very short haired result is required.

8. Hair should be dry when using electric hair clippers.

9. The essential feature of a graduated neckline is that there is no clear definition where the hairline ends and the neck begins.

10. The razor used on wet hair.

CHAPTER 13

1. Contraindications to the provision of a wet shave are: open cuts or sores on the face, muscular swellings, contagious skin conditions.

2. Should the client's skin be cut while shaving, powdered alum of ferric chloride should be applied to a clean sterile dressing and then held against the cut.

3. Two reasons for tensioning the skin while shaving are to provide a closer shave and to prevent cutting the client.

4. Steam towels provide moist heat that relaxes the client, improves the softening action of the lather, cleanses the skin's surface.

5. Astringent lotions are applied to the skin following a wet shave to close the skin's pores and help prevent infection.

6. First time over shaving strokes usually go with the direction of beard growth.

7. Sharps should be placed in an appropriate container which is then incinerated by a specialist company.

8. The benefit obtained by shaving the nape hairline is a cleaner defined outline, which will last longer.

9. The benefits from facial massage are improved muscle tone and relaxation.

10. Use of cold towels following a facial massage will close the pores, preventing the spread of infection and reducing any discomfort that may be experience if an astringent lotion is applied.

CHAPTER 14

1. Infectious conditions are those diseases passed on by contact with a contaminated object.

2. You should protect yourself from the effects of chemicals when working on clients by wearing protective gloves and overalls.

3. The term used for abnormal hair loss is Alopecia.

4. The female head louse lives for approximately one month.

5. The most effective treatment for split ends in hair is to cut them off.

6. The period of hair growth is known as Anagen.

7. The three areas of the hair root are the follicle, the bulb and the papilla.

8. The three layers found in hair are the cuticle, the cortex and the medulla.

9. A fungal parasitic scalp disorder is Tinea Capitis (ringworm).

10. The term given to excessive production of sebum is Seborrhea.

16 Your personal skill check

This section may be photocopied for your continuing personal use, to enable you to evaluate your own development towards competence and to help you identify existing competence.

HOW TO USE THE SKILL CHECK

Within the table you will find questions about your job or hairdressing experience. In the adjacent columns you will tick as appropriate. If you never carry out a particular task tick the first column, if you carry out the task out but need considerable guidance from your trainer in doing this tick the second column, if you can carry the task out without guidance from others then tick the third column and if the task forms your normal job role which you carry out on a regular basis you should tick the fourth column. If you intend to claim existing competence or wish to plan how your competence will be assessed, use the evidence identification section to help identify where and how you will collect this.

This table may help you identify which award is most appropriate to your competence, needs and expectations.

LEVEL 1 AND 2 HAIRDRESSING

Task	Never done	With assistance	Little assistance	Regularly done	What evidence of competence I have to support this claim across the range
Consult with clients on technical services and products Level 2					
Advise clients on after care procedures and future salon services Level 2					
Maintain effective working relationships with clients Levels 1 and 2					
Shampoo and surface condition hair and scalp Levels 1 and 2					
Apply conditioning treatment to hair and scalp Level 2					
Dry hair into shape; include detail of the range of hair and drying techniques Levels 1 and 2					
Create a finished look on dry hair Level 2					
Cut hair to produce a variety of one length looks Level 2					
Cut hair to achieve a variety of layered looks Level 2					
Cut hair to achieve a variety of fashion looks Level 2					

Task	Never done	With assistance	Little assistance	Regularly done	What evidence of competence I have to support this claim across the range
Carry out basic perms on virgin hair and chemically treated hair Level 2					
Neutralise perms and relaxers Levels 1 and 2					
Relax hair using a range of straighteners Level 2					
Add temporary colour to hair Level 1 and 2					
Add semi-permanent colour to hair Level 2					
Permanently change hair colour Level 2					
Create highlight and lowlight effects in hair Level 2					
Remove colouring and lightening products from hair Levels1 and 2					
Attend to visitors and enquiries Levels 1 and 2					
Schedule appointments for salon services Levels 1 and 2					
Handle payments from clients for the purchase of services and retail products Level 2					

Task	Never done	With assistance	Little assistance	Regularly done	What evidence of competence I have to support this claim across the range
Organise your own work role Level 2					
Work with others as part of a team Levels 1 and 2					
Improve your personal effectiveness within your job role Level 1 and 2					
Maintain, replenish and rotate stock daily Levels 1 and 2					
Make cost-effective use of resources Levels 1 and 2					
Maintain personal health, hygiene and appearance Levels 1 and 2					
Operate safely in the salon Levels 1 and 2					
Set hair to achieve a variety of looks Level 2					
Dress out set hair Level 2					
Dress long hair into style Level 2					
Cut facial hair into shape Level 2					

Task	Never done	With assistance	Little assistance	Regularly done	What evidence of competence I have to support this claim across the range
Cut hair to achieve a variety of short layered looks with different neckline shapes Level 2					
Remove hair by shaving Level 2					
Provide face massage Level 2					

Index